STRUCTURE

VISION + VALUE SERIES

STRUCTURE
IN
ART
AND IN
SCIENCE

EDITED BY

GYORGY KEPES

George Braziller, New York

8374 CONTENTS

Expelled from the smaller, friendlier world in which previous centuries of men moved with confidence born of familiarity, we are today compelled to cope with an expanded scale of events in a big, alien, re-defined world. In order to live freely and fully in our new world, we have to learn to map its strange vistas, to discern in them harmonious structures appreciable by our visual sensibilities, and to arrange our lives in conformity with the new perspectives.

So far, we have failed to live up to the twentieth-century challenge. Science has opened immense new vistas to us, but we have failed to utilize our new technology fully or to share it wisely. We shrink from accepting the deeper and richer sense of life, uniquely inherent in our twentieth-century world, that is sometimes touched upon in the best moments of our best artists. We have not yet found our places in this broadened world.

We should realize that our failure was caused, in truth, by the blinders that we have put around our eyes, hearts, and minds. Sometimes ignorance, sometimes inertia, but mostly fear that we may be forced into giving up vested interests has kept us from pooling our knowledge, feelings, and power, and has thus prevented us from finding our potential twentieth-century selves.

Most persons who work in cultural and scientific fields recognize that the past century and a half has brought a fragmentation of experience, an explosion of knowledge into many self-contained disciplines, each with a wildly growing and increasingly private language. The infant Macaulay thought that he knew everything worth knowing. He did not—although a Macaulay, he was nonetheless an infant—but in his day this accomplishment was still conceivable. Today, it is manifestly impossible. And the accelerating spiral of knowledge, with its concomitant centrifugal thrust, is driving us apart. Clearly, our sense of a cohesive world is endangered by a crisis in communication. We are lost in a new scale of existence, with once-familiar relations uprooted, and habits and purposes displaced.

If we recognize and meet the challenge of our stage of history, we can live fully and sanely in contemporary terms, without danger of cultural impoverishment. We need, therefore, to find new centripetal forces that can hold our common understanding together and realize for us the spirit of our times.

We now speak many different dialects, to be sure, but these are dialects of the same basic language. We can communicate—that is, combine and reinforce our knowledge with that of other men—by stimulating the circulation of ideas and feelings, finding channels of communication that can interconnect our disciplines and enable us to see our world as a connected whole. G. G. Simpson, the paleontologist, has commented that, as organic evolution was brought about by interbreeding, so our further cultural evolution today will come about through broadscale "interthinking."

There must be feedback to our central scale of values from the new vistas that confront us in the scientific, technological fields. Our senses need to bridge these vistas and catch their meanings, their human overtones and undertones. Using our extraordinary vision, we can fashion such bridges.

Vision is a fundamental aspect of human insight. It is central in shaping our physical, spatial environment, in grasping the new aspects of nature revealed by modern science, and above all in the experience of artists, who heighten our perception of the joys and sorrows of life. Artists are living seismographs, as it were, with a special sensitivity to the human condition. They record our conflicts and hopes; and their immediate and direct response to the sensuous qualities of the world helps us to establish an entente with the living present.

As the twentieth century has grown older, most of our artists have recoiled upon themselves. They lack orientation in the total contemporary world, which, if they but knew it, holds as much promise as it does menace. Their honest response has been to scream their isolation. In frantic retreat, many of them have adopted a scorched-earth policy and burned their most valuable cultural belongings. Cornered and confused in a "horror of lost self," as the poet Robert Lowell puts it, some of them advertise brutality as vitality and intellectual cowardice as existential self-justification.

Artists today come together in small groups in great cities. There, in little circles that shut out the rest of the world, initiates share one another's images. They generate illusory spontaneity, but miss the possible vital, deep dialogue with contemporary intellectual and technological reality. It is unfashionable today, if not taboo, for artists to think and act on the broad terms of cultural and social ideals. No doubt, moralizing in art can lead to creative suicide, just as market-policed and state-policed art can lead to the murder of artistic honesty. But the other extreme—lack of intellectual curiosity and rejection of commitment—leads to emaciation of artistic values.

It seems that the overwhelming task of creating the new scale of modern science has used up some of our most vital intellectual and emotional equipment. When a vital part in a complex machine is worn out or out of adjustment, it is wiser to stop the mechanism than to grind on to destruction. Engineers, in such a case, devise arrangements that ensure orderly shutdown when a part gives way. It may be that what our cultural life is now experiencing is such a "failure to safety," as the engineers call it. Our artists may thus have served us by preventing disaster.

Nevertheless, emotional return to the archaic, ancestral cave is an obvious failure to function in contemporary terms—however necessary. Let us not mistake this temporary standstill for a genuine answer to our deeper long-range needs. We cannot renounce the dimensions of the twentieth century—the new vistas, the scientific triumphs—because they were bought with human distress. We may suffer from exposure to the new scale, but it is necessary for us to go ahead and meet its challenge.

Only complete acceptance of the world which is being born can make our lives genuinely acceptable. Such acceptance implies, above all, two concrete tasks. One, in every field of human endeavor we must advance to the furthest frontiers of knowledge possible today. Two, we must combine and intercommunicate all such knowledge so that we may gain the sense of *structure*, the power to see our world as an interconnected whole.

Structure, in its basic sense, is the created unity of the parts and joints of entities. It is a pattern of dynamic cohesion in which noun and verb, *form* and *to form*, are coexistent and interchangeable; of interacting forces perceived as a single spatio-temporal entity.

It is no quibble to separate the notion of structure from such related concepts as order, form, organized complexity, whole, system, or *Gestalt*. Each historical era seeks and needs a central model of understanding. Structure seems central to our time—the unique substance of our vision.

The most powerful imaginative vision is structure-oriented. As old connections crumble away, inevitably our creative efforts seek out new ordering principles to replace the old. In different fields, for different reasons, the new ordering relations are being accepted as fundamental. Scientists, for example, have come to recognize that the key properties of different materials are determined according to the way in which atoms, the basic building units of nature, are arrayed and the way in which they are joined together, rather than, as once assumed, according to the elemental stuff of the material. The differences among solid, liquid, and gaseous states are explained by the patterning of their atoms, the relative closeness of their molecules.

From inorganic structures to plants and animals, from the movements of animals to their social behavior patterns and to human relations, structure is central. A dramatic focus of structure awareness has been reached through understanding of the molecular structure underlying the genetic mechanism of living forms. Inherent in the spiral structure of the complex molecule DNA is the ability to reproduce itself. Thus, a built-in program of growth and development is provided for an infinite variety of unfolding structures of living forms.

Structure is also central to our understanding of our ways of understanding. Studies of our perceptual and cognitive processes by *Gestalt* psychologists show that psychological events do not occur through the accumulation of individual elements of sense data but through the coordinated functioning of clearly patterned networks of sensation determined by structural laws. Investigations into the nature of language show that the structural properties of languages have far-reaching effects on ways of thinking. "For my part," says Bertrand Russell, "I believe that partly by means of the study of syntax, we can arrive at considerable knowledge concerning the structure of the world."* For the structure of a person's thought processes is based on the complex structure of his language, which offers him certain categories and denies him certain others. Complementing the mathematical and logical study of language, such complex tools as high-speed computers help to shed light on the various structural inter-relations of the nerve centers.

Creative exploration in the arts has yielded significant parallels with scientific investigation. The early twentieth-century painters who were still hoping and trying to embrace the complete vista of contemporary conditions looked for structural principles in art. Instead of aiming at an illusionary rendering of what they could see around them, they invented images and patterns. Clear, unmodulated surfaces, abstract shapes, and simple, basic colors devoid of emotional overtones were used as building blocks. "True architecture," wrote Juan Gris, a thoughtful pioneering painter of this period, "cannot be broken up into different pieces, each of which is autonomous and exists alone. A fragment of architecture will be no more than an odd, mutilated object that ceases to exist when it is removed from the one place where it belongs. Construction, then, is merely the imitation of architecture. The technique of painting is flat, colored architecture, and not construction. It is based on the relations between colors and the form that contains them."** This passionate involvement with image-building process had its great ancestor in Cézanne, many of whose successors built consistent, legible pictorial structures from the direct data of inner sensibility.

The most impressive manifestation of this interest is seen in contemporary architecture and engineering. Pier Luigi Nervi, whose work has almost symbolic significance in this context, has observed that the ever-increasing size of contemporary buildings has brought the problem of structure to the forefront. Structure has assumed such formal importance as to become the central feature of architectural design. In structural architecture, the forces of compression, tension, moment, and shear become a clearly legible

*An Inquiry into Meaning and Truth, p. 438.
**"On the Possibilities of Painting," Trans-Atlantic Review, Paris, vol. I, p. 482.

pattern of stress and just as clearly legible a pattern of neutralization of stress—visible and comprehensible, demonstrative of the properties of the materials with which the forms are executed.

The editor of these volumes has a long-standing, stubborn belief that, all signs to the contrary notwithstanding, we may build, from our rich, many-faceted range of structural knowledge, a structure of structures, a new sense of interdependence between knowledge and feeling—and thus a keener and more profound awareness of our own time. Led by this conviction, he has conducted seminars at the Massachusetts Institute of Technology for fifteen years, with the participation of scientists, architects, and artists. It was hoped that students might gain confidence that they could combine and reinforce their knowledge with the knowledge of other fields by stimulating the circulation of ideas and feelings, finding channels of communication that interconnect disciplines, and suggesting the interconnectedness of the world as a whole.

The volumes of this series have grown out of those seminars. The contributors include some of the original participants and others whose papers have been written especially for these books.

The present volume consists of two parts: the first is concerned with the scientific approach to structure and structuring processes in nature; the second with the structures and structural principles found in man-made forms, especially in artistic communication and expression.

Three scientific essays form the first part. The first two essays deal with structural laws in inorganic nature. The third examines the role of the exterior world in the structuring of our interior world, of our thoughts and perceptions. All suggest the new and immensely rich resources of images that we can derive from our present knowledge of the world and of the minds of men.

The papers in the second part of the volume develop this suggestion further. They demonstrate how our new insight into structure can be adapted to provide keys, metaphors, that illuminate new vistas and adumbrate new solutions to the problems faced in creating our technical and artistic environment.

The first essay, by Lancelot Whyte, gives a synoptic view of the structural principles operating on the many levels of our physical world. Whyte emphasizes the close structural interconnections of the basic building blocks of our universe. He points out that we are moving away from the classical science of simplicity toward a modern science of ordered complexity: we are replacing the older concept of atomism with the newer concept of structure—structure that is not a rigid scaffolding for a schematized reality, but an aspect of the morphologic process.

One observation by Whyte underlines the significance that his remarks about our current knowledge of the physical world can have for all of us. He describes the crisis of the physicist working on the frontiers of science. For him, the physical world has become complex and abstract. Its visual content, which first impelled him to explore and explain, has become faded and has lost its original strength and inspiration. Whyte maintains that, if he were to return to the three-dimensional world of human eyes and hands and seek anew to interpret its everyday forms, fresh insights would be obtained and his disillusionment dispelled. The physicist's crisis bears upon the whole scope of this volume, for science and art share the problem of vision, in its deeper and creative aspects. The immediate data of vision are continually looked upon afresh wherever they are to be reorganized in a higher context.

Cyril Smith, in the second paper, examines a more limited aspect of the physical world in which structural patterns have a more prominent and obvious meaning. Smith examines the same structures at different microscopic levels, and reveals the complex inter-relationships of structure at different levels of existence. He leads the reader from the microscopic level of crystal patterns to the level of structural organizations visible to the naked eye. Particularly significant is his discussion of pattern matching, of congruence in structure from one level to the next. This discussion has importance for the creative arts, for it points to a possible correspondence between the structural patterns of the physical world and structural needs of the human mind.

The contribution of the psychologist Richard Held deals with the most recent investigations of the relationships between objects of the outside world and their projected inner images. We open our eyes and look out on the world of objects, shut them and blot out the scene. We walk among and between things in the world and gain different perspectives on them. How, why, and when we can find correspondences between the objects and their "effigies," as Held calls them, is basic to our understanding. What structural correspondences we can discern between the outer and the inner world is fundamental to the manipulation of our environment and also to our inner richness. It is assumed that some kind of order among the stimuli coming from the environment must be reserved in the retinal image. What the nature of this order is and the way it is translated into inner images plays a significant role in furthering our understanding of our relationship to our environment.

The second part of the volume is concerned with the arts in the broadest sense. Each essay suggests ways in which our understanding of structure in nature can guide us in creating forms—whether of design, such as buildings and cities, or of communicative expression, such as paintings and sculptures.

The essay by Bronowski is a thoughtful introduction to this section. It examines the correspondences and analogies to be found in every age between the scientific image and the artistic vision of the physical world.

"Conceptuality of Fundamental Structures," by Buckminster Fuller, provides an inspiring bridge between our comprehension of the structural principles of nature and the potential application of this knowledge to creation of man-made forms.

The next five essays all deal with man's building activities as he structures the physical environment around him. In his "Structure, Construction, and Tectonics," Eduard Sekler analyzes and clarifies our use of these key terms, which recur in the subsequent essays.

The two short papers by Luigi Nervi examine the vital link between the designer's knowledge of physical processes and his own creativity. The creative man involved in the shaping of physical forms must have a deep respect for the nature of his material and for the structural pattern that this material dictates. Nervi's essays emphasize the importance of the interplay between imagination and the cold facts of task and material if the designer is to arrive at new, authentic solutions of form problems.

The essays by Nervi, the Smithsons, and Maki and Ohtaka are concerned in differing degrees with the structuring of our environment, and are progressive in breadth of scope. Nervi deals with individual forms, such as buildings and bridges; the Smithsons, in "On Building toward the Community Structure," with the redevelopment of Sheffield University, in which the basic task is to organize large-scale units in relation to one another; Maki and Ohtaka, in "Collective Form," with gigantic cityscapes beyond the present scope of our imagination. The latter two essays, dealing with community and metropolitan organization, embody concepts of utmost importance today. The increasing magnitude and complexity of entities to be structured is the newest and most challenging problem of twentieth-century design.

The last five papers deal with problems of structure in communication and artistic expression. I. A. Richards is directly concerned with structure in linguistic communication; he points out that language structure has assumed sociological importance as an educational tool.

Structure and communication—this "key-and-lock combination," as Richards puts it—are also the subjects of H. L. C. Jaffé's essay "Syntactic Structure in the Visual Arts." Jaffé makes clear that abstraction and concern with structural problems in painting of the last eighty years have been prompted essentially by a will to communicate. He also points out that many contemporary artists reject a structural approach. He concludes that the concept of painting as a semantic system, or language, is really a "pre-eminently social" concept, because "language and communication are closely linked to the contact of man with his fellow human being."

Max Bill, like Nervi and Jaffé, discusses the structural approach in the visual arts, and points out how the order of natural forms and natural law inspires the creative imagination. To Bill, structure is dynamic; uniformity and invention "manifest themselves [in art] as rhythm . . . a work of art grows out of the general structure by means of a rhythmic order." This statement is significant: in contrast to other approaches, it suggests a common structural basis for both external nature and the processes of human perception.

If Jaffé and Bill share a high regard for nature's structural laws as nourishment for art, Richard Lippold represents a dissenting voice. He shows that the importance of structure is by no means self-evident to all contemporary artists, for some of whom the intellectual turmoil of this century has destroyed it. Noting the rapidity with which modern science demolishes its theories, he maintains that the only approach to nature left to art is the illusion afforded us by our senses and feelings. Despite this playful evasion and the sophisticated manner in which Lippold divests structure of reality, his essay contains a clear and significant truth: ordinary appearances *are* illusion, not the concrete reality we once thought.

The concluding essay touches upon the central theme of this volume: the correspondence between the structural characteristics of natural and artistic forms. In her "Concrete Painting as Structural Painting," Margit Staber seeks a definition of structure that enables us to formulate this conjunction of scientific and artistic, of rational and aesthetic. She finds a suitable modern definition in the biological writings of Wolfgang Wieser: " 'Structure' should be understood to mean a network of relationships of elements or of elementary processes. Structures appear wherever elements combine into a meaningful whole whose arrangement follows definite laws. The wholeness in which we discover and examine structures we call a 'system.' Thus, there are inorganic, organic, sociological, and technical systems . . ." To these, Staber would add aesthetic systems.

Those central images and concepts which provide the key to man's inner world, and thus to the way in which he organizes the outer world around him, are different for different stages of history.

To the Greeks, form was essential—form and matter. Upon chaotic matter, God or man imposed a marvelous intelligence, creating form. The Greek universe was smaller than ours, shaped in accordance with the perceptual limits of the naked human senses. Human ingenuity could stretch those limits—but not far. There was not room enough for a thing to have more than one matter or more than one form.

The universe we know today stretches endlessly beyond the reach of our unaided senses. The same "thing" has one type of organization on the level at which we examine it with our eyes and hold it in our hand, and another type of organization at the level of nuclear mechanics. In between, there are many intermediate levels, each as real as the next. The key modern concept of structure encompasses arrangements on all these levels and many, many more.

The world as a set of structural systems does not divide into the two territories of scientific knowledge and artistic vision. Rather, both our scientific understanding and our artistic grasp of the physical world exist within a common structure of motivation, communication, and knowledge. Every step toward the mutual enrichment of art and science brings us closer to full realization of our own potentials.

To reach what we all hope for, to become worthy of an environment worth living in, we must do what we can to bring our outer and our inner worlds together—renew the ancient marriage of art and science, art and nature. To rely solely on one area of our knowledge may lead us into blind alleys. Let us heed the warning given us by John Milton in *Areopagitica,* 1644:

"We boast our light, but if we look not wisely on the sun itself, it smites us into darkness . . . The light which we have gained was given us, not to be ever starting on, but by it to discover onward things more remote from our knowledge."

STRUCTURE: VISUAL DOCUMENTS

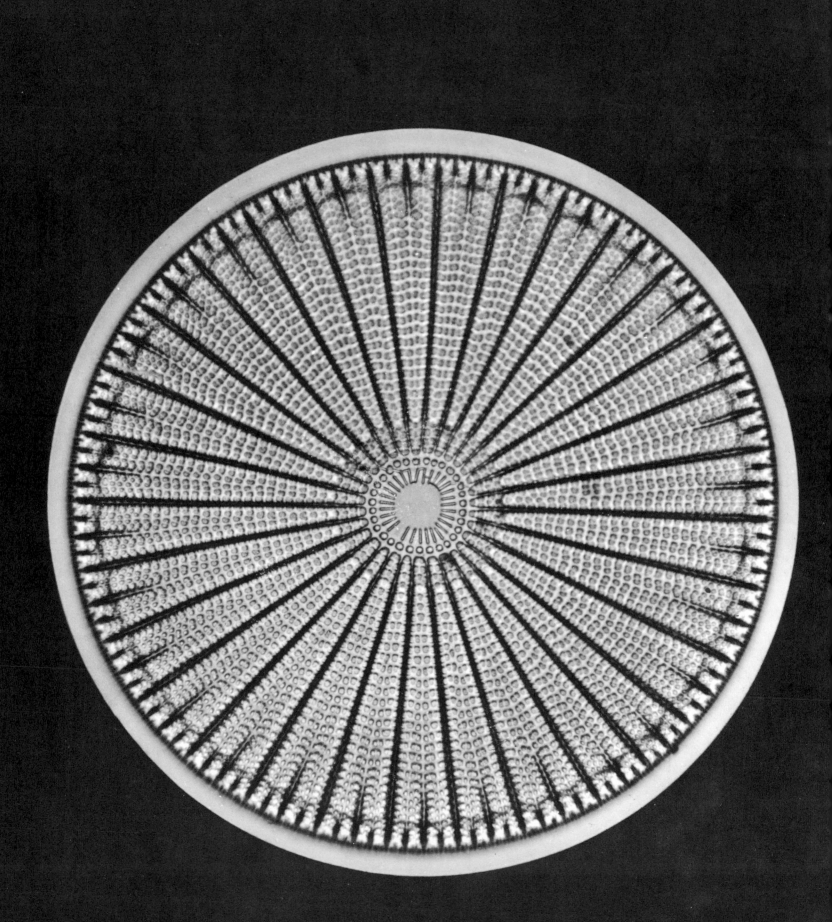

Photomicrograph of the Arachnoidisus Ehrenbergii by Max Posner.
(Photo Courtesy Bausch and Lomb)

Photomicrograph of Pure Hafnium by H. P. Roth,
Massachusetts Institute of Technology.

X-ray Diffraction Pattern of Beryl.
(Photo Lane, Eastman Kodak Company)

Photomicrograph of Vitamin A by Jack Kath.
(Photo Courtesy Merck, Sharp and Dohme)

Photomicrograph of a Cross Section of a Twig by I. W. Bailey,
Harvard University.

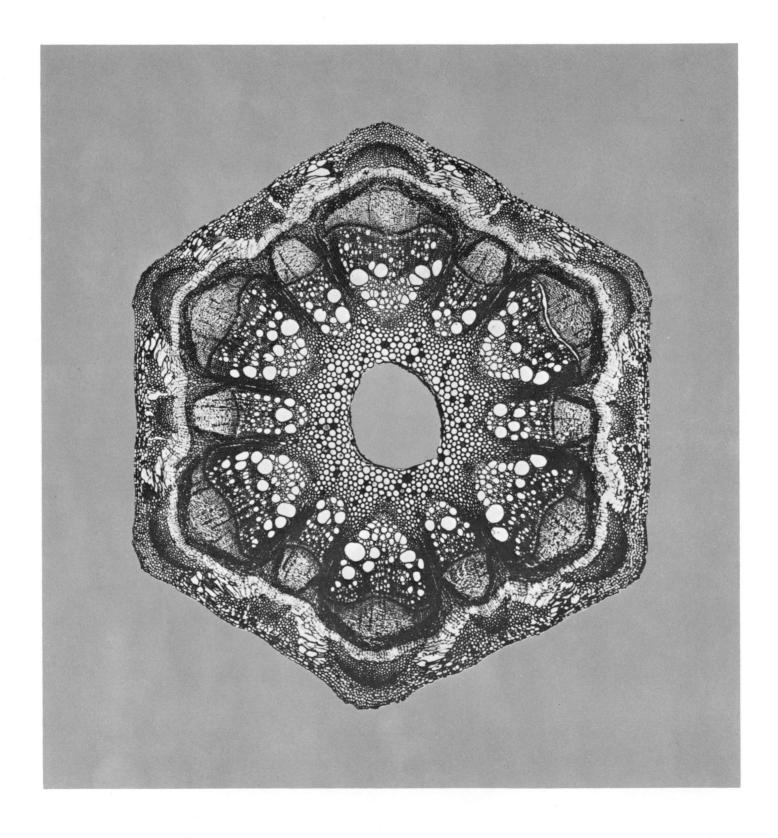

Frei Otto and collaborating team members (J. Koch, C. Hertling,
G. Minke, H. Habermann, G. Reuer, B. Romberg).

Structure Studies, 1962–63.

a: Chain model, hexagonal grid of equal meshes.
b: Chains in curved frame.
c: Frame with double curved spring net.

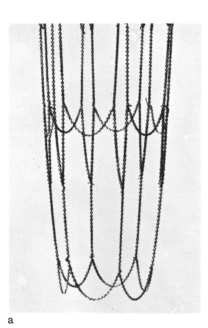

a

b

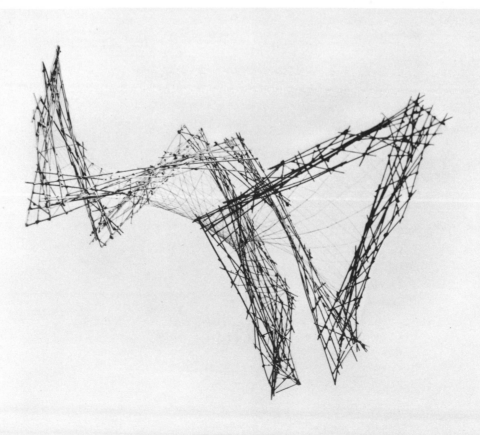

c

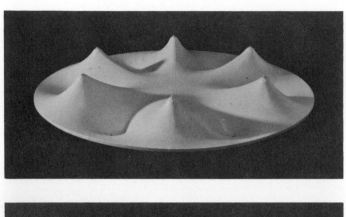

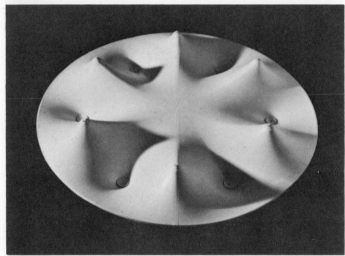

Horacio Caminos.
Model for a type of membrane roof structure, 1963.

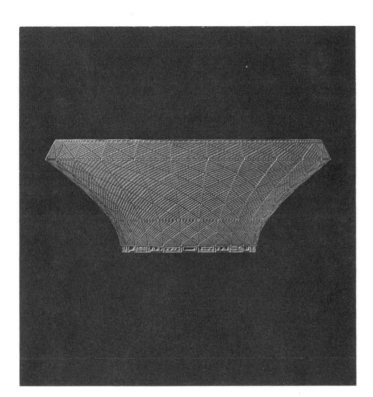

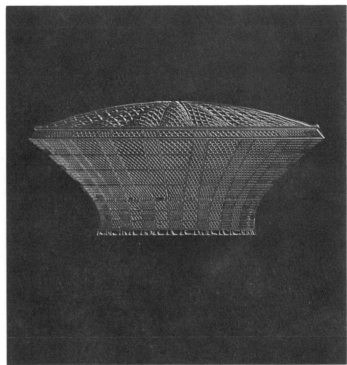

Horacio Caminos.
Project for World's Fair building, 1963.

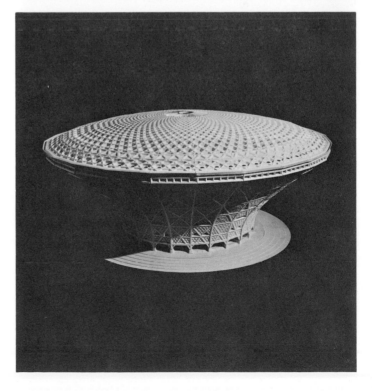

Frei Otto and collaborating team members
(J. Koch, C. Hertling, G. Minke, H. Habermann, G. Reuer, B. Romberg).
Tent Structure, Yamburg, 1962–63.

a: Exterior at night.
b: Interior view.

a

b

Ewald Bubner and Frei Otto.
Steel welded church tower, Zehlendorf Schonow, 1962–63.
View shortly after erection, before bells installed.
Ground plan 6′ x 6′; Height 75′.

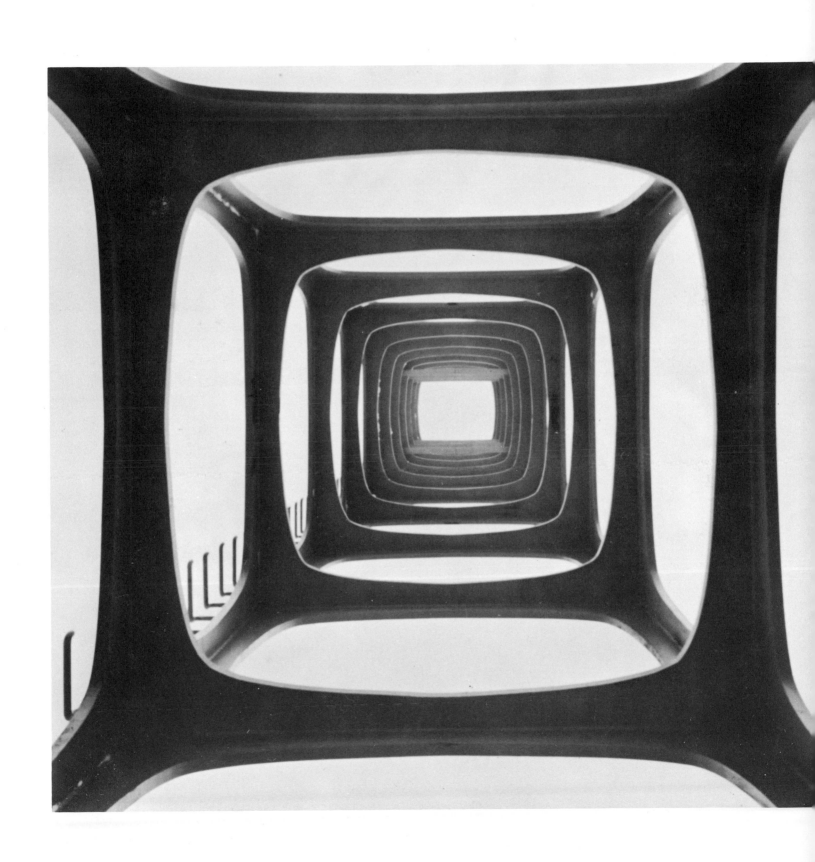

Eduardo Catalano

a. Structural system based upon the combination of twelve portions of the double curved warped surface called hyperbolic paraboloid. By varying the number of these four-sided portions, the relationship among them, their position in space, the length of their edges and the angles formed by these, a great number of different spatial combinations can be conceived. True structures are not rigid *unic* forms, but systems in equilibrium that allow multiple spatial transformations without losing their structural properties.

b. City as a system: Proposed structural network for a new city, based upon a system of life, circulation, growth and transformation. The structural network starts at the center with a simple orthogonal organization that grows outward, changing in geometry, dimensions and use, while preserving its unity and continuity. The system, as the regulatory structural idea, can suffer topological transformation as the result of changes in time, topography and human needs, without losing its basic structural properties.

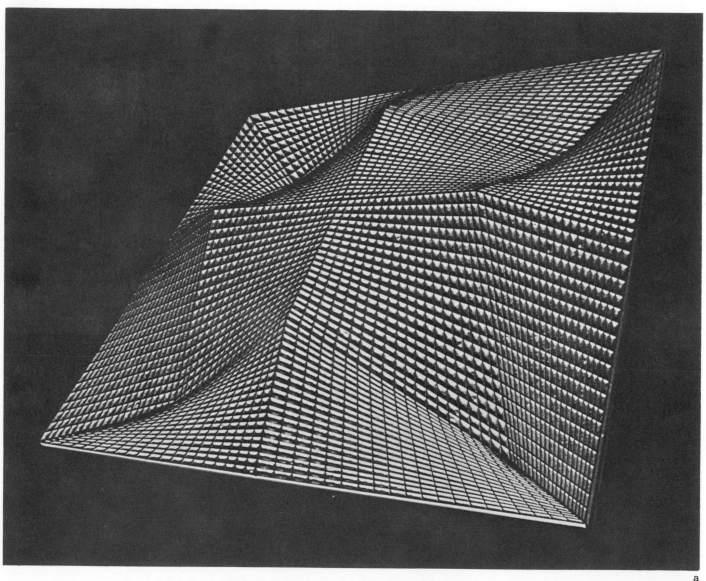

a

b

Juan Gris. *Guitar, Book and Newspaper*, 1920. Pen and ink drawing.

Piet Mondrian. *Rhythms of Lines and Colors*, 1937.

El Lissitsky. *Proun 19D,* 1922? Gesso, oil, collage on plywood.
Museum of Modern Art, New York. Katherine S. Dreier Bequest.

Kasimir Malevich. *Suprematist Architectural Drawing*, 1924.
Museum of Modern Art, New York. Purchase Fund.

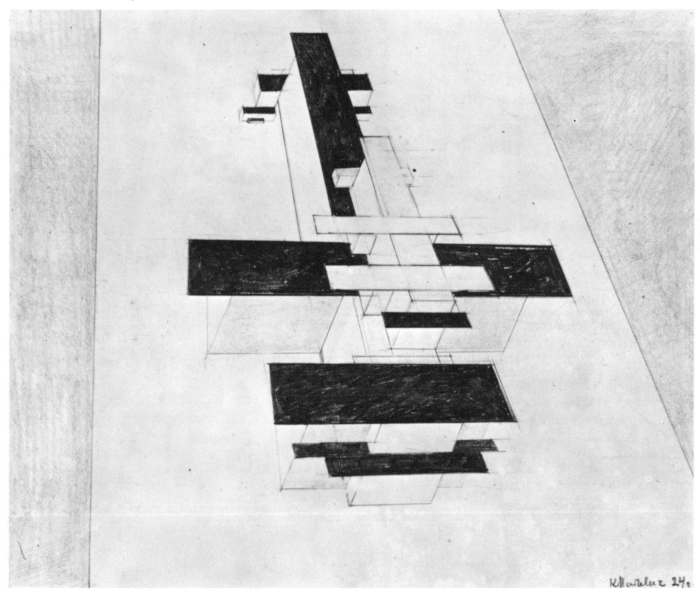

Georges Vantongerloo. *Composition, Green-Blue-Violet-Black, Number 105*, 1937. Solomon R. Guggenheim Museum.

Naum Gabo. *Linear Construction*, 1942–43. Plastic.
The Phillips Collection, Washington, D.C.
(Photo Herbert Matter)

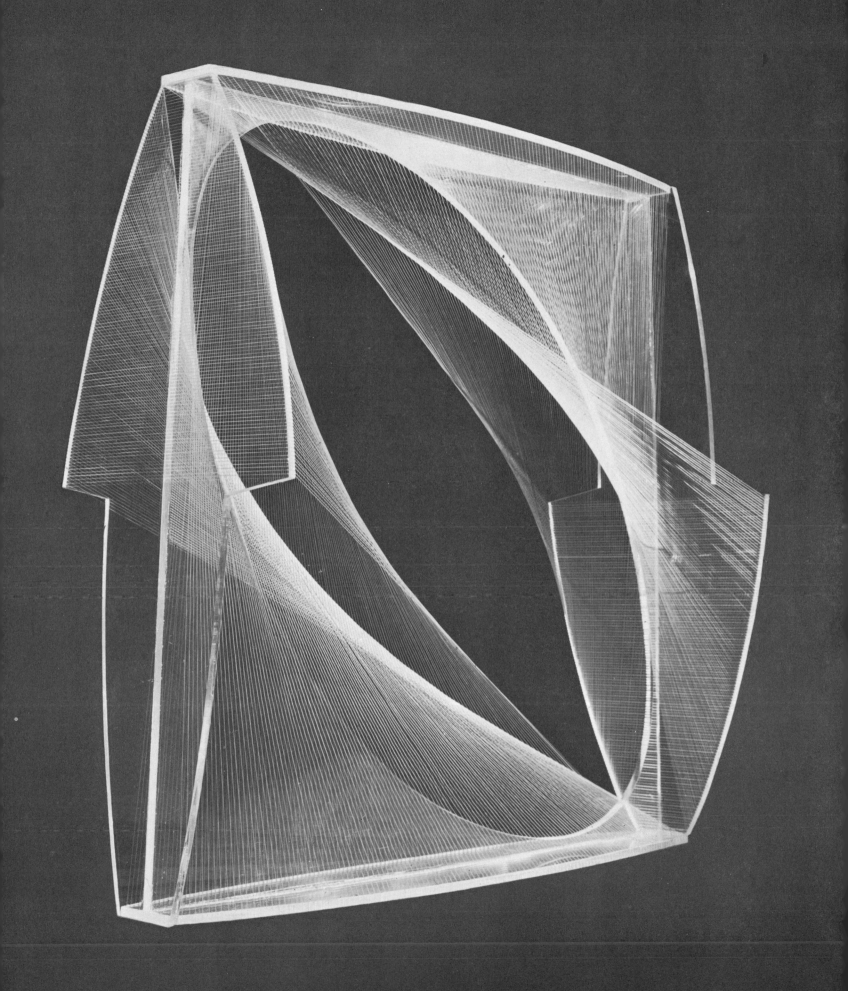

LANCELOT L. WHYTE   ATOMISM

STRUCTURE AND FORM

A Report on the Natural Philosophy of Form

This paper has two main themes. The first is an objective report: During this century the attention of scientists has been moving from the simple towards the complex, with the result that a modern conception of STRUCTURE is, for some purposes, replacing the older conceptions of ATOMISM and of FORM. The second is a suggestion: The unifying natural philosophy of the coming period may be a morphology, a doctrine of form viewed as structure.

These summaries need explanation. But I think it will be seen that they imply something that everyone can understand; a shift of emphasis from two contrasted ideas: from relatively isolated small units and over-all shapes, towards a single comprehensive and precise identification of structural patterns and their changes. Arrangement, configuration, organization, structure, ordering—these are now key words. What underlies this verbal fashion? Greater attention to complexity.

This affects all who deal with visual material: not only artists, designers, and architects, but everyone intrigued by the practices and malpractices of science. Caution is needed in passing from physics to the practical and fine arts, but we cannot prevent science from casting seeds in all directions. For the old problem of part and whole is being seen anew, in terms of *partly ordered structure*. In his long pursuit of order in nature, the scientist has turned a corner. He is now after *order and disorder* without prejudice, having discovered that complexity usually involves both.

This is an astonishing liberation from the natural preference for order of the adaptive organism in man, and a great gain in objectivity. If this interpretation is correct the natural sciences in the coming period will be even more strongly marked by an explicit combination, already evident in quantum mechanics and the biology of populations, of structure and statistics, of definite stable forms and random variation. But for many purposes ordered structure comes first. For "random" always means the absence of some particular type of order, and mere coexistence in three-dimensional space in itself implies the presence of a subtle and pervasive ordering.

The excitement of this uninhibited exploration of form as symmetry and asymmetry, or as order and disorder, is already beginning to be shared in wide circles in the U.S.A. and elsewhere. The present series is the latest of many signs of a spreading wave of interest in the problems of spatial form. This may be partly due to the fascination of the fresh landscapes of physics and biology and the new *sense for structure* characteristic of many intellectual activities during this century. I think of this as a *new school of form*, a community marked, not by any achievements, but by the desire for clarity in a realm which still lacks its organizing ideas. The members of this school are looking to the concept of visual form to provide clues to the unity of knowledge. (What better way to retain the spirit of youth than to sense hidden meanings and promises of new vistas in the forms around one?)

This enthusiasm for form is all very well, but it encounters a serious difficulty. Few can follow the specialist languages of the exact sciences. Moreover even if conceptions of spatial form and transformation can be made precise and comprehensive, and used to bring greater coherence to the special sciences, this will take time. Patience is necessary, and a long historical view.

Form has always fascinated enquiring minds and invited interpretation. "Who then . . . discriminates between the atoms, gathering them or scattering them . . .? . . . they needed an intelligent artist to put them together." (St. Dionysius, the Great, of Alexandria, fl. 240 A.D.). And today a scientist can still call form "the magic of the world" (A. M. Dalcq, 1951).

A first fact of human existence is that we live out our lives in three-dimensional space surrounded by definite shapes, constant or changing. Yet we are here fundamental ignoramuses. Why *three* dimensions? Is the *three* fact or artifact? Why regular forms at all, amidst so much confusion? Morphogenesis is still a mystery in nearly all realms. Only in a few restricted fields, to be considered in a moment, do we know how anything has come to have the shape it has, in terms of basic principles.

If we ask the quantum theorist for help, we find that he is busy in an abstract pseudo-space calculating "observables," which unfortunately are not the shapes that are observed with naked eye or microscope, but rather "measurables" in a technical sense. For this reason he finds it difficult to say why complex macro-molecules, bio-molecular helices, organic tissues, organisms, brains, solar systems, or galaxies have just the forms they have. His methods are not designed to answer the general problems of form, and he is tempted to say that the "initial conditions" which lead to the production of particular forms are not his concern.

It takes a rash mind on the flying trapeze of thought to attempt the leap from the abstractions of basic physics to the directly perceived forms of the visual universe. But it is worth the risk. Our visual experience is immediate, while the abstractions of fundamental science are for some purposes much too abstract.

First some *explications*. Definitions can be stimulants, but they are often hypnotics. I have tried here to elucidate some of the most useful meanings, in the context of this paper, of the terms we are employing. Other contributors may use them differently.

ATOMISM means broadly the reduction of complex data to finite numbers of fixed unit factors. In physics these factors are ultimate material units. Here "ultimate" should mean that the units have no internal structure which can undergo change, and "material" should mean that they are permanent or at least subject to some rule of conservation. The "elementary particles" of the quantum mechanics of 1930-60 are primary constituents in that theory. But they may not be primary in a future theory, for there are too many and most of them are unstable. Thus the status of physical atomism is uncertain at the date of this report, I believe because it is in course of being transformed into a theory of structure, with structural rather than atomic laws in the traditional sense.

FORM has myriad meanings. I use it here either in the vague sense of overall shape of line, surface, or volume, or more precisely for the ordering of parts which determines these shapes—the context will show which. The need for brevity forces us to consider form without color; this may limit the validity of the argument. While atomism recalls a long accumulation of discoveries, form is a reminder of ignorance. (Form is a challenge to the inquisitiveness of the scientist, while the artist may do better without analytical understanding.) When the exact ordering of parts is in mind, it is usually better called:

STRUCTURE, for this is form seen inside, as a definite arrangement, static or changing, of localizable parts, such as a pattern of points. Structure must be at least partly ordered, or it is lost in complete chaos, if such a thing exists. To the mathematical logician structure is a formal system of relations of certain logical types, and the emphasis in all usages is on the relations rather than on the terms or entities which they relate. Structure is thus the antithesis of matter.

This is not a proper definition. For we do not know what "order" must mean if it is to apply in all realms of science, and "formal" begs important questions. The thought of an adaptive organism, after a thousand generations of trial, error, and improvement, can never be independent of experience. Indeed the ivory tower of the most abstract logician—such as Bertrand Russell pondering on logical structure in Trinity College, Cambridge, around 1905—is at the heart of the battle for human adaptation. For the realm of structure, understood in its full generality, appears to be as wide as that of analytical reason. But we do not yet know what structure means where there is complex transformation. There the structure of change is still obscure.

The importance of the modern conception of logical and mathematical structure began to dawn on many thinkers around the turn of the century. Heinrich Hertz, though he did not use the term structure, showed his understanding of its significance in his "Principles of Mechanics" (1894), and Russell and Whitehead's "Principia Mathematica" (1910) marked its formal coming of age. But structure still awaits its Newton, to display its empirical power, and its Lucretius, to sing the philosophical emancipation which it promises.

The philosophy of structure is monistic, relational, precise, and potentially comprehensive. Unlike those ontologies of existence which seek permanent substances beneath appearances, such as extended matter or thinking mind, it accepts as alone objective a changing pattern of relations. Isomorphic structures are indistinguishable; structure is all there is. It is not for us to look *behind* the tapestry of transient patterns for anything more permanent and comforting, though in the changing structure itself certain aspects may be conserved: perhaps field energy or point particles.

Our concern here is with spatial structure, steric arrangements in three dimensions. (I shall not consider topological structure; for that see Bronowski's paper.) The spatial structure of natural systems extends from the galactic structure of the universe through many levels down to molecular, atomic, and presumably some ultimate structure—still unidentified—which may provisionally be pictured as a pattern of discrete points obeying either atomic laws or some unknown kind of pattern law. There is thus a hierarchy of structures.

But at whatever level one is interested the first questions for those wishing to analyze visual material of any kind are: What symmetries or other regularities are present? What lengths or angles are associated with these regularities? With what random or irregular features are they combined, and what changes do they undergo?

What, then, are the *structural principles of inorganic and organic forms*? What is known, and what unknown, of the basic rules determining the static or stationary forms of physics and biology, their formation and transformation?

The rub is in the word "basic," for I am using it in a radical sense. Science is not always an endless pursuit of closer approximations and more powerful theories. Occasionally it comes to a full stop. "Basic" is here employed to mean that in relation to a restricted realm examination over at least twenty-five years has suggested that the principle is comprehensive, and therefore may be assumed to be definitive, as against one that is clearly incomplete, and therefore certainly not final. This is a severe criterion, and its use leads to a one-sided picture of the state of knowledge. That is its purpose; we are interested in reliable principles, not those that are likely to let us down.

Here is an example, a perfect one in every sense, from the realm of static three-dimensional forms. The decade 1885-95 stands out in the history of science. For it was then proved, once and for all, that the equilibrium structure of every homogeneous crystal at a low enough temperature must correspond to one of 230 distinct types of symmetry. The "must" is the direct consequence of the simplest conceivable assumptions applied to three-dimensional space. 230 types are possible, no more, no less, and no Einstein can ever question this, the most firmly established mathematical conclusion concerning anything in this three-dimensional universe. Here the science of form has touched bottom. This is the paradigm for all knowledge of spatial form, because it is static and geometrical and exploits to the full the steric character of our space.

Indeed the mathematical theory of perfect crystal structure sets an embarrassingly high standard. For if we look for equally lucid and reliable conclusions regarding the arrangement of the constituent parts of other systems, we shall be disappointed. This table shows the principal constituents of some important kinds of systems:

Systems	Major Constituent Parts
Atomic nuclei	Protons, neutrons
Atoms	Nuclei, electrons *
Simple molecules	Atoms * * ?
Complex molecules	Atoms
Liquids	Molecules
Bio-molecular aggregates	Grouped atoms
Organisms	"Hierarchies" of atomic groups
Solar system	Sun, planets *
Galaxies	Stars
The Universe	Galaxies

An asterisk is placed opposite those three types of system for which basic principles have been established covering equilibrium or stationary forms. A second asterisk is given in one case, to indicate that for very simple molecules there is also a theory of their formation and disintegration which may conceivably be definitive. The query is there because until complex molecules are covered one cannot be certain that the best way of treating simple ones has been found.

Gases are omitted, since in the ideal gas there is no characteristic quantitative structure. But liquids are included, because they contain transient orderings of groups of molecules, though there is no good theory of these as yet. Like organisms, ordinary liquids display a subtle blend of order and disorder that has not yet been identified, though that may not be far off.

In this examination *homo sapiens* gets $^3/_{10}$ for stationary forms and possibly $^1/_{10}$ on transformations, and so would lose any title to his name, but for his brilliance on crystals. Still he has learned something, and we can ask: what basic structural principles regarding equilibrium forms have already been established?

The answer is that the concept of *potential energy* has proved effective in those realms where it can be applied, and that *stable equilibrium forms are those which minimize the total potential energy of the structure*. Without going into details, one may say that this principle is nearly equivalent to stating that *stable forms are those in which all arbitrary variables have vanished*, the system having reached a state of higher symmetry or equivalence in which all such freely variable differences or deformations have been eliminated. Thus stability is usually associated with symmetry and maximum electro-magnetic neutrality, though this "rule" cannot be applied generally. As a structure moves towards its equilibrium or stationary form, various asymmetries, such as deformations, electrical polarizations, unbalanced magnetic twists or spins, etc., tend as far as possible to disappear. To give one example: the form of the solar system, though rather complex, is stable because the factors (differences, asymmetries etc.) making for rapid progressive changes have already worked themselves out, so that to a high approximation only cyclic processes remain, though these are subject to continual perturbations.

But there is an awkward limitation to the conception of potential energy. By itself it implies nothing regarding initial conditions and it only yields results when assumptions are made about the arrangement of the parts at the beginning of any process. Some type of structure has to be assumed, before the potential energy principle can be put to work. Moreover exact science can say little regarding the conditions of formation of stable complex systems when their three-dimensional character plays an essential role. It can select some kind of symmetry, and get to work on that, but is embarrassed by symmetry transformations, though atomic physics is now approaching this basic issue. Most scientists are good on linear and planar patterns, but have not trained themselves to think easily about steric arrangements, especially when they are chiral (skew or twisted) and heterogeneous, and undergo changes. Perhaps as a result of this the transformations of the elementary particles of physics are still in some respects almost as puzzling as the transformations of the human embryo. There must exist rules of three-dimensional construction and reconstruction which nature uses all the time, but we haven't yet identified them. We have to get more accustomed to steric thinking in general, not only in the relatively simple cases of rectilinear perspectives.

One can summarize the position thus. The *energy principle* sets restrictions on the processes that can occur, but of itself says little about structure, for that is not its task. On the other hand *atomic methods* are able to follow the ultimate parts in simple cases, but tend to get lost when the structure is too complex or the energy too great. What is lacking is an appropriate instrument of wide applicability for following the simple transformations of complex systems.

But a number of interesting tentative rules have already emerged from the study of complexity. Some of these have already been mentioned; others, which may be dim announcements of some of the *motifs* of a future symphony of structure, must be left as mere hints:

Asymmetries and differences can vanish, but new ones cannot arise, in isolated structures.

Stability is a property of certain structures; their individual parts often come and go.

Complex structures may possess simple modes of vibration, deformation, and transformation.

Structures can form coordinated working hierarchies (organisms) in some manner not yet understood.

In these hierarchies certain persisting structures of high specificity tend to extend their own pattern, by replication or otherwise.

After this quick glance at the science of structure we turn to the natural philosophy of form, seen through *the antithesis of atomism and form*.

These terms are the banners of two temperaments, two extreme expressions of human mentality. The first stands for analysis, logical precision, and quantitative accuracy. *Reduce everything to discrete unit factors, and investigate their properties!* This is the only systematic procedure for advance yet invented, though it often leads to the neglect of order and it does not always work. It is represented by Democritus, Russellian logical analysis, most exact science, and every kind of intellectual fission.

The second honors the integral object, the entire character of anything, either seen from outside or still forming in our own minds. *Respond to form, and neglect analysis!* This is a call to surrender to the *Gestalt* qualities of visual experience, but it is not an intellectual method, and its followers must generally be content with isolated intuitions of the winged truth. Goethe, the *Gestalt* psychologists, and the pre-structural organismic biologists illustrate this response. But so also do the mathematical theories of symmetry and invariance, which are concerned with global properties of complete systems and are fortunate shots; these crown past work, they are not methods for advance.

On a superficial view these two extremes appear as mutually exclusive alternatives. But on examination, or on a historical view, they are seen to be complementaries, two aspects of a single comprehensive response to experience not yet fully developed: the complete recognition of ordered structure. Analysis is indispensable, but it must issue in the study of order. Total responses to integral forms are natural, but can be matured by knowledge of structure. This is not a forced synthesis, arbitrarily imposed from outside; it is just the way things are. The analytical mind must ultimately come to order, and the form enthusiast come to earth and accept structure. For that is how this universe is made.

The period of satisfaction with analysis reached a climax during the last decades of the nineteenth century. At the very moment when classical kinetic atomism gained its greatest successes, a new movement was beginning concerned more with relations, collective ordering, and integral forms. Von Ehrenfels recognized (1890) the *Gestalt* properties of perceptual forms, and simultaneously (1885–95) the mathematicians of crystal structure identified the symmetry forms of linear arrays of identical units. Relativity theory and quantum theory are factors in this movement, the first stressing observable two-term relations, the second more complex observable patterns of relations. The physics of our century is thus engaged in a struggle to eliminate from its thinking those features of classical (pre-1900) physics which resulted in the provisional neglect of the more complex aspects of spatial order.

Leaving aside the psychological and historical aspects, we can look deeper into the logic of the situation. What precisely was the limitation in classical atomic methods which caused the relative neglect of order and form?

It seems that the method of treating the properties of ultimate small units as fundamental only works well when a rather small number of variables—say less than five or ten—is adequate for some purpose, as in simple molecules and homogeneous fluids. When it comes to complex partly ordered systems, rich in structure and form, this classical method is very clumsy if we are interested in ultra-structure and its changes. Nature seems to be saying with all possible emphasis: *the laws of complex systems are not written in terms of quantitative properties of their localized constituents, but in terms of . . . ?*

The missing phrase may be *global properties and collective parameters*, such as the characteristic constant angles, and ratios of linear steps, in the lattices of crystals. But crystals are static and what are needed are not constants, but collective variables determining the simple processes of complex structures. For example, all bio-units, from enzymes to animal organs, have highly complex structures, but relatively simple functions. The chromosome system in the nuclei of cells is fabulously complex, but it can behave as a unit, it can undergo simple tranformations, and with the aid of the cytoplasm it somehow guides the development of a coordinated organism. While its spatial structure is highly complicated, that structure must be capable of undergoing global changes which can be represented by a very few collective variables. But no-one has yet discovered a general rule showing how the most suitable collective variables are to be identified in physical or biological systems. Yet it seems that overall form and morphogenesis must express the operation of such collective parameters.

This great antithesis: atomic units with their properties *versus* the partly ordered form of the whole, stands as a barrier delaying all attempts to advance. This is so in many fields, but perhaps most clearly in what is surely mis-called "molecular biology", for the concept of separately identifiable *molecules* must here be misleading! Take the genes, or genic regions, arranged in sequence along the chromosomes. In certain respects "genes" behave as unblending units, in others as cooperative elements in an ordered complex. This dual behavior pattern confuses statistical analysis, and will not be fully understood until more is known of the rules of ordering that determine the functional stability and efficiency of both the chromosomal system and of the organism as a whole.

Again we see that the ordering is the weak spot in present knowledge. But it seems that the stage has been reached, say between 1900 and 1960, when a science of ordered complexity is taking over from the classical science of simplicity.

This is an open ended report, ending with some conjectures on *what lies ahead*.

Science is in an awkward situation. Knowledge has become a single stupendous web of facts, known to be multiply inter-connected but lacking appropriately powerful organizing ideas. The burden of uncoordinated facts is insupportable. Mathematics no longer unifies.

Moreover traditional methods are known to require overhauling. Energy, with its transformations, pervades the whole field, but says little about particular complex structures, while particles are mere ghosts of what they were. Statistical methods are as dangerous as they are powerful, for they tend to conceal the prior assumptions involved in their use. The variety of symbolisms is so great that the humble letters of the alphabet have to perform multiple tasks.—Is all this elaboration necessary to describe *visual* observations?

A few physicists, though expert in the realm where cumulative achievement has been most marked, have even suggested that the long advance of their science may have passed its culmination, that comprehensive unifications marked an age already past, and that the ordering passion of the theoretical mind may be faced with an indefinite period of frustration. This is mainly because high energy theory is becoming so complex, abstract, and void of visual content, that it no longer promises an adequate reward for effort.—Yet the tracks of high-energy particles are simple forms in *visual* space!

Such discouragement is certainly premature, for no well planned raid on the enemy headquarters has yet been made. No comprehensive and radical analysis has been made of all known spatial forms, that is of all the kinds of spatial order, disorder, structure, and complexity already known to exist in this universe, not merely as reflected in recent successful theories. Scientists are not free from the common weakness of the human mind, of paying little attention to facts to which current ideas do not point. When more intellects of physics grow weary of their occupation with high abstractions, and try to interpret anew the forms we perceive in this three-dimensional world, as some are now attempting to do, new vistas will appear, and present fears be forgotten. The immediately given must be seen afresh if significance is to be recovered. So I believe.

I know of no better way to define the frontiers of today's knowledge of form and structure than to put some questions which are already clear enough for us to be aware of our ignorance:—

What is chaos, if forms emerged from it? How much order must be ascribed to the "initial conditions" of the cosmos? Do the laws of nature describe the production of order, or only a timeless order?

What is the universal relation of structure to process?

Do universal laws of structural process, of formation, transformation, and decay, exist—comparable to the great conservation principles?

What is the relation of the two cosmic tendencies: towards mechanical disorder (entropy principle) and towards geometrical order (in crystals, molecules, organisms, etc.)?

How do contrasted parts cohere to form stable working units?

What is the status of skew and screw forms in natural law?

What kind of ordering of parts underlies the functioning coordination of organisms?

How does the inherited structural pattern in the germ cells produce mature functional forms?

How does the brain discern patterns and make its own?

What marks those genic arrangements that produce, in appropriate environments, beautiful bodies and minds?

I end by confessing a private doubt: is it sensible to write an article on form so short that it must neglect color and beauty?

Annotated Selected Bibliography

These books have been chosen to give the best introduction to the general philosophy of atomism, structure, and form. They are arranged in order of first publication.

A Bibliography on "Form" covering 160 titles is given in "Aspects of Form" (1951), see below. On narrower applications and recent developments (e.g. structure of atoms, bio-molecular aggregates, statistical methods, etc.) readers should consult specialists.

First publication

1917   D'Arcy W. Thompson, *On Growth and Form*.
An illustrated classic on the mathematical representation of organic forms, as seen fifty years ago. (Abridged by J. T. Bonner, Cambridge University Press, 1961.)

1917   L. J. Henderson, *The Order of Nature* (Harvard University Press).
Not explicitly on form, but providing valuable background.

1919   Bertrand Russell, *Introduction to Mathematical Philosophy* (Macmillan, New York).
Chapters 5 and 6 treat the logical relations and structure which underlie most exact reasoning and are implicit in every rational philosophy of nature.

1920   F. M. Jaeger, *Lectures on the Principle of Symmetry and its Application in all Natural Sciences* (Cambridge University Press).
A general survey of its subject at that time; still broadly reliable. Illustrated.

1932   D. Hilbert and S. Cohn-Vossen, *Geometry and the Imagination* (Chelsea, New York). Translated from German.
On curves, surfaces, point systems, topology, etc. Geometry used by a master to provide an introduction to mathematics as a whole. Illustrated.

1936   J. Needham, *Order and Life* (Yale University Press).
A classic attempt to discern the nature and deployment of the order which underlies biological form.

1951   L. L. Whyte (Ed.), *Aspects of Form: A Symposium on Form in Nature and Art* (Midland Paperback, 1961).
Eleven contributors survey their fields at 1950. Illustrated. Chronological survey and Bibliography.

1952   H. Weyl, *Symmetry* (Princeton University Press).
Masterly treatment of its theme, illustrated from nature and art.

1952   A. Portmann, *Animal Form and Pattern* (Faber, London).
This elementary illustrated work is included to provide a more concrete visual approach.

1954   L. L. Whyte, *Accent on Form* (Harper, New York).
Conjectures on the unifying role of the concepts of form and formative process.

1961   L. L. Whyte, *Essay on Atomism, from Democritus to 1960* (Wesleyan University Press).
Historical and philosophical survey. Short Bibliography.

CYRIL STANLEY SMITH

STRUCTURE SUBSTRUCTURE SUPERSTRUCTURE

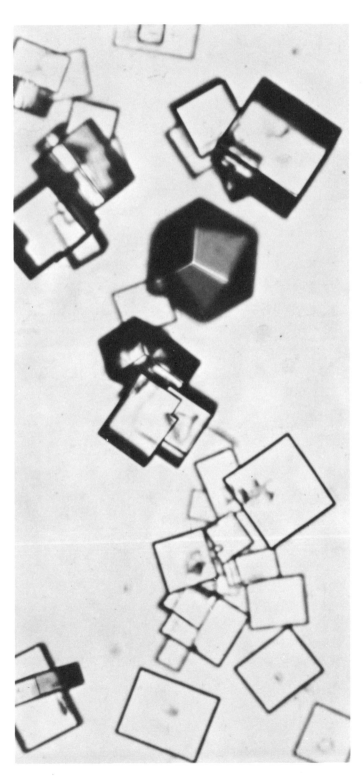

Anyone who works with the microscope for an intellectual or practical purpose will frequently pause for a moment of sheer enjoyment of the patterns that he sees, for they have much in common with formal art. What follows is an attempt to extend into a more general field some views on the nature of organization and relationships that arose during many years of study of the microstructures of metals and alloys.* In a landscape painting of the Far East, a rock in the foreground with cracks and crystalline texture is often echoed in a distant mountain with cliffs, chasms, wrinkles, and valleys; a tree may be related to a distant forest or a turbulent and eddied stream to a distant tranquil pond. Each part with its own structure merges into a structure on a larger scale. Underlying structures which are only imagined are necessary as a basis for the visible features. The connectivity of all is suggested by the branching tree-like element of the design. Both separateness and continuity are interwoven, each necessary to the other and demonstrating the relationship between various features on a single scale and between the units and aggregates on different scales. There is a close analogy between a work of art which suggests an interplay of dimensions and the real internal structure of a piece of metal or rock which results from physical interactions between the atoms and electrons composing it.

The study of microstructure on the scale within the range of the optical microscope (dimensions between a micron and a millimeter) is a somewhat old fashioned branch of science, and it still involves a high degree of empirical observation and deduction. Far more "highbrow" is the rigorous science and simple elegant mathematics of the ideal crystal lattice considered as point groups in space. The whole field of crystal structure, mathematically developed in the nineteenth century by Bravais, Federov, and Schoenflies, was experimentally opened up by Von Laue and especially the Braggs in 1912-13, using the diffraction of X-rays to reveal and to measure the periodicities and symmetries in the arrangement of planes of atoms in crystals. But the mathematical physicist must simplify in order to get

* The converse relationship between aesthetics and metallurgy—the influence of the techniques discovered by craftsmen making works of art upon the development of the science of metals—was discussed at some length in my *History of Metallography,* Chicago (1960).

Fig. 1. Group of polyhedral salt crystals growing individually from solution. Magnification x 200. *(Photo by C.W. Mason)*

a manageable model, and although his concepts are of great beauty, they are austere in the extreme, and the more complicated crystal patterns observed by the metallurgist or geologist, being based on partly imperfect reality, often have a richer aesthetic content. Those who are concerned with structure on a superatomic scale find that there is more significance and interest in the imperfections in crystals than in the monotonous perfection of the crystal lattice itself. Like the biologist, the metallurgist is concerned with aggregates and assemblies in which repeated or extended irregularities in the arrangement of atoms become the basis of major structural features on a larger scale, eventually bridging the gap between the atom and things perceptible to human senses.

The symmetry of crystals in relation to decorative ornament has been treated by many writers, none better than by Hermann Weyl in his *Symmetry* (Princeton, 1952). The patterns of crystal imperfection are less commonly known, despite their prevalence and despite their relationship to so many aesthetically satisfying forms in which regularity and irregularity are intricately intertwined.

Crystalline Aggregates and Foam Structures

Aggregates of crystals have structures which are defined by the atomically thin layer of disordered material between the crystals. Many characteristics of their shape are shared with simple undifferentiated biological cells and the simplest common soap froth. In all these, the pertinent features are the two-dimensional surfaces that separate volumes of matter which, on this scale, is featureless. Two-dimensional interfaces are necessary to define the separate identity

Fig. 2. Raft of tiny uniform soap bubbles showing "grain boundaries" where zones of differing orientation meet. Magnification x 7.

Fig. 3. Deeply etched section of a piece of niobium metal, showing network of grain boundaries revealed by selective attack at grain boundaries. Magnification x 200. *(Photo Courtesy R. J. Gray, Oak Ridge National Laboratory)*

Fig. 4. Surface of over-heated aluminum sheet showing the beginning of melting at the grain boundaries. Magnification x 4. *(Photo Courtesy British Non-Ferrous Metals Research Association)*

Fig. 5. Etched section of silicon-iron alloy, showing the junction of three crystals. (This is an historic photograph, taken in 1898 by J. E. Stead.)

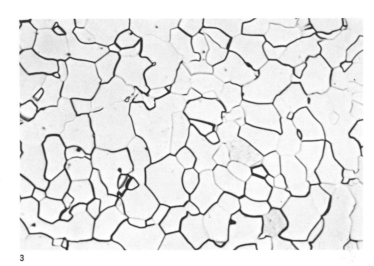

3

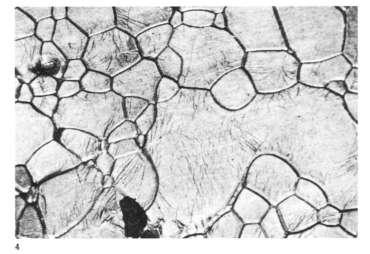

4

5

of things in three dimensions. Junctions of the interfaces themselves produce linear (one-dimensional) features, and these, in turn, meet at points of zero dimension. This interaction between dimensions, the very essence of form, is expressed in mathematical beauty as Euler's Law. This simply states that, in a connected array, the number of points minus the number of lines plus the number of surfaces and minus the number of polyhedral cells is equal to one, i.e.,

$$n_0 - n_1 + n_2 - n_3 = 1$$

where n_0, n_1, n_2, and n_3 are the numbers of zero, one, two, and three-dimensional features. There are no limitations to this, beyond the requirements of simple connectivity. Even more than Euclid, hath Euler gazed on beauty bare.

A pure metal, when cast (or, better, after a little working and heating) has a structure like that of Carrara marble—hosts of little crystals packed together irregularly. The units do not look like crystals, for they lack the symmetrical vertices and plane faces of a regular polyhedron, but internal order is there nevertheless. Although for centuries man has been fascinated by the geometrical shape and glitter of natural crystals, he has only recently come to see that the essence of crystallinity lies not in external shape but in the uniformity of the relationship of atoms to their neighbors within the crystal. A single isolated crystal growing from a solution or melt can grow uninterruptedly in accordance with the dictates of the atomic steps on its surface. Usually this will result in a simple polyhedron (Fig. 1), reflecting the internal order because of its effect on the rate of growth in different directions. If many crystals start to grow in the same region, sooner or later they will interfere with each other. Neighboring crystals differing in no way whatever but in the direction of their atom rows in space cannot join without some imperfection. Figure 2 illustrates this. It is a magnified photograph of an array of tiny uniform bubbles floating on soapy water. The lines of disorder that form between the differently-oriented areas of regularly arranged bubbles in this two-dimensional model are believed to be closely analogous to the planes of disorder constituting the boundaries between the three-dimensional crystal grains in metals, rocks, and other polycrystalline materials. The boundaries are a source of both strength and weakness and they provide the sites for the beginning of any crystalline change. Though themselves invisible except at the extreme limit of resolution of modern electron and ion microscopy, they differ so much in energy from the body of the crystals that they are easily revealed as lines of enhanced chemical attack (Fig. 3), early melting (Fig. 4), or they can be inferred from the sudden change of

crystal direction revealed by some kinds of chemical attack on the surface (Fig. 5). Patterns like these can often be seen with the naked eye on the weathered surface of a cast brass doorknob or hand rail, or internally in clear ice which has been kept just at its melting point for several hours.

Now these boundaries, which on an atomic scale are just imperfections in a uniform stacking array, on a larger scale themselves become the basis of structure. They are, in fact, films of matter, distinguished by structure rather than composition. They must surround every crystal and extend in foam-like fashion continuously through the entire mass.

Fig. 6. Froth of irregular soap bubbles showing a cellular structure analogous to that of metals. These bubbles were blown between parallel glass plates and are essentially two-dimensional. Natural size.

Fig. 7. Pattern of craze lines on a glazed ceramic surface. Magnification x 1.5.

Fig. 8. The shape of cells in human fat tissue. Magnification x 400. *(Photo by F. T. Lewis, Courtesy American Academy of Arts and Sciences)*

Fig. 9. Crystal grains of a metal (brass) separated from an aggregate, showing the natural shape of crystals when packed randomly into contact with each other. Note the frequency of pentagons and curved surfaces.

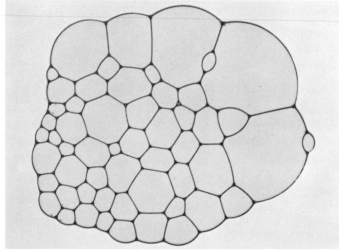

6

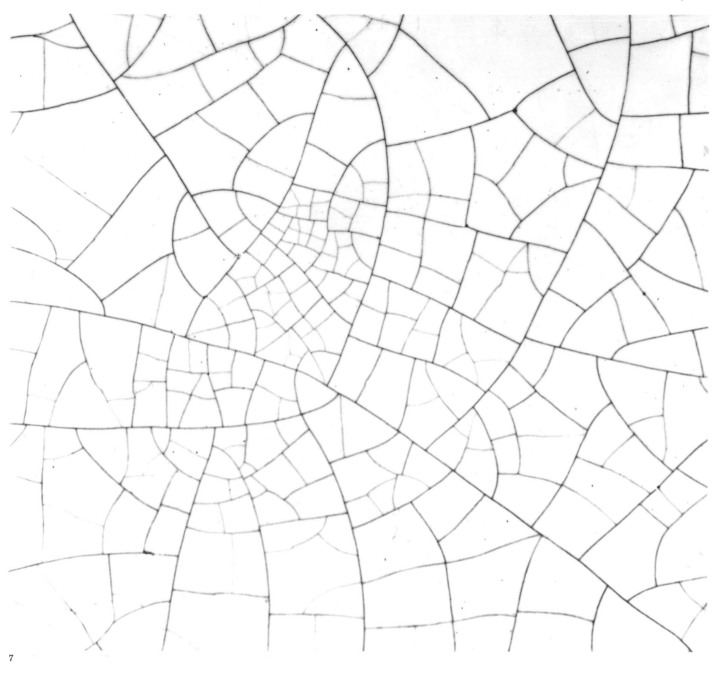

7

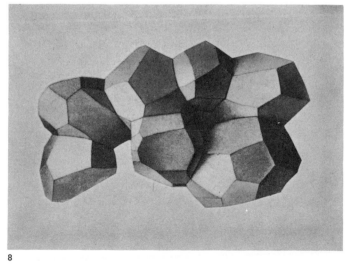

8

9

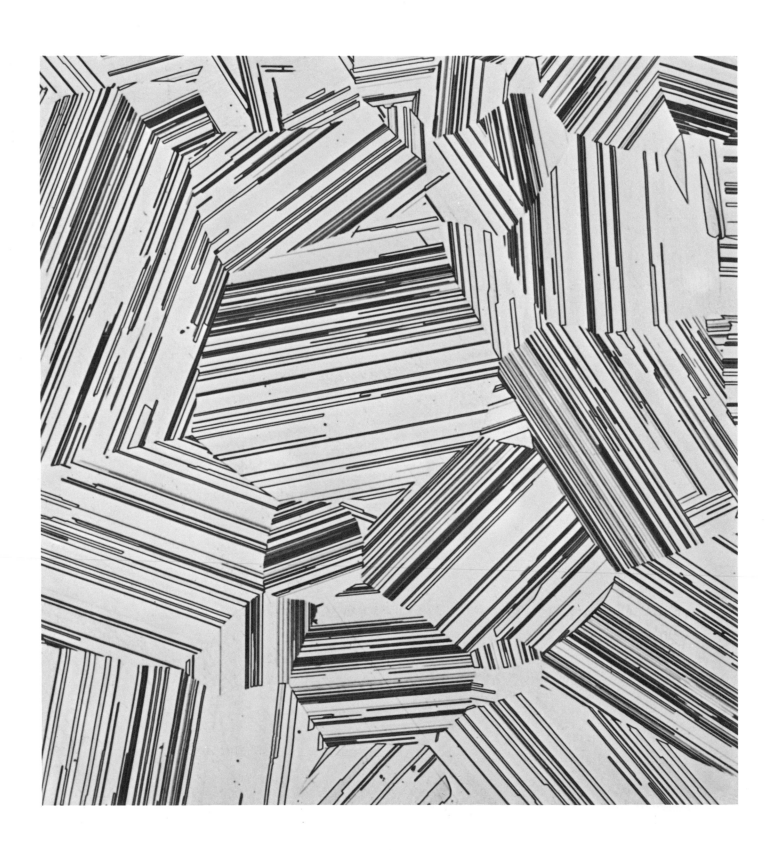

Fig. 10. Duplex crystals with bands of different composition in exact orientation relationship within one grain, but forming an over-all foam structure like a pure metal, here seen in a copper-silicon alloy, worked and annealed. Magnification x 300. (This is an etched section.)

Fig. 11. The same alloy as Fig. 10, deformed by cold rolling.
Note the heterogeneity of the distortion. Magnification x 300.
(Photo by B. Nielsen, University of Chicago)

Fig. 12. Transformation structure in a hardened nickel steel, showing interference between differently oriented crystals growing within the same crystalline matrix. Magnification x 250. *(Photo by Daniel Hoffman)*

Fig. 13. Branching pattern in corrosion of stainless steel in uranyl sulphate solution. Magnification x 100. *(Photo Courtesy R. J. Gray, Oak Ridge National Laboratory)*

12

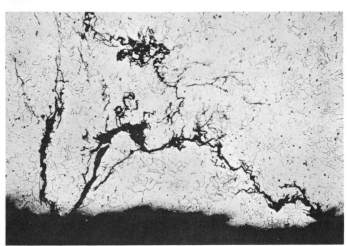

13

Having high energy and mobility, they tend to adjust to a configuration of small area, which makes them join each other always in groups of three at an angle of 120°, just as do the films in a froth of soap bubbles. In a mass of large bubbles of irregular size (Fig. 6) there will be differences in pressure between adjacent bubbles to match the surface tension in the curved films and to reconcile the 120° angle with the necessity to fill space. Since three bubbles meet at each junction, Euler's law requires that the average bubble in an infinitely extended array must have exactly six sides, but there is no requirement that each one be a hexagon, only that if there are some with more than six sides, there must be a matching number with less. The froth therefore, though lacking long-range symmetry, nevertheless has very definite rules as to its composition. It is pleasing in appearance

because the eye senses this interplay between regularity and irregularity. The topological requirements of space-filling rigidly determine the relationships of the whole, but allow any one cell to be of pretty much any shape, while surface tension equilibrium requires only that the films be at 120° to each other at the point of meeting, always three together, and it produces the pressure differences that are needed to balance the resulting curvatures. Beyond this, all depends on the accidents which brought a bubble of a particular size to a given place and surrounded it with its particular neighbors, each also with its private history.

It is interesting to compare a two-dimensional soap froth with the topologically similar but geometrically different pattern of craze marks in a ceramic glaze (Fig. 7). Though the cracks divide the surface into cells meeting three at each junction, the geometry is different from the froth because the cracks must follow the direction of stress in the glaze and a new crack joins an old one perpendicularly.

A foam in three dimensions is a bit more complicated, but depends on the same principles. To divide space into three-dimensional cells, at least six two-dimensional interfaces must meet at each point; and if surface tension dominates they will join in groups of three at 120° to each other along lines, forming cell edges, which meet symmetrically at the tetrahedral angle of 109.47°. (The angle whose cosine is minus $\frac{1}{3}$.) This configuration of three-, two-, and one-dimensional junctions is repeated at every vertex. Curvature is necessary to connect adjacent vertices and to reconcile the short- and long-range needs. Because the polygons (cell faces) must be in groups which close around each three-dimensional cell, the average polygon will have a smaller number of sides than the hexagon which connectedly fills space in two dimensions. No single plane polygon can meet the requirements, for it would have to have 5.1043 sides in order to have corner angles of 109.47°. The best solution that has been proposed corresponds to a fourteen-sided body with six plane four-sided faces and eight double-curved hexagonal faces, the mixture of polygons having on the average $5^{1}/_{7}$ sides. This curious irrational number is of the utmost importance, though it is little appreciated. Certainly it is responsible for the prevalence of pentagons in nature. It is probably behind the five-fold symmetry of plants and the five fingers and toes of animals. Frequent pentagonal faces are readily seen within a three-dimensional froth of bubbles on a glass of beer and they occur also in such disparate bodies as human fat cells or metal grains (Figs. 8 and 9). Pentagons are frequent but not universal, for the ideal num-

Fig. 14. Dendritic growth of an iron crystal. Magnification about x 300. (This historic drawing was made in 1876 by the Russian metallurgist D. K. Tschernoff.) In large steel ingots such crystals sometimes measure several inches in length.

Fig. 15. The surface of an ingot of antimony, showing dendritic crystals which have grown to interference with each other. (This pattern was the mystic Star of Antimony of the alchemists.) About natural size. *(Photo Courtesy The Science Museum, London. Crown copyright)*

ber is an irrational one and pentagonally-faced polyhedra alone cannot fill space.

It should be noted that the external shape of the crystals in Fig. 9 reveals nothing of their inner order, for the shape depends on the property of the disordered boundary, not the ordered crystals that are separated. A more obviously crystalline geometric structure occurs when a second crystalline phase originates in direct contact with a pre-existing one, for it automatically forms in whatever definite orientation gives the lowest energy of the interface. Not infrequently two different kinds of crystal grow in symbiotic relationship with each other, forming duplex oriented units which serve as the basis for an irregular foam-like aggregate quite similar to that formed by crystals of a single substance. Examples of such oriented duplex structures are shown in Figs. 10 to 12.

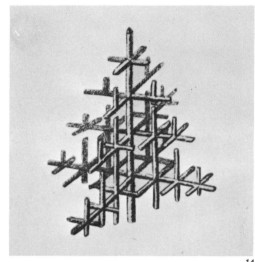

14

15

Fig. 16. Pattern of ridges formed by a crack moving in a crystal of a brittle compound of copper and magnesium, Cu_2Mg. The crack proceeded from the top to the bottom of the figure. Magnification x 300. *(Photo Courtesy Duane Mizer, Dow Metal Products Company)*

Branched Structures

The soap froth is the archetype for all cellular systems which for any reason are constrained toward a minimum area of interface. A quite different type of structure, though a common one, is the one that results from the growth of isolated individuals in the branched form best illustrated by a common tree. This occurs whenever a protuberance has an advantage over adjacent areas in getting more matter, heat, light, or other requisite for growth. Such structures occur in electric discharge, in corrosion (Fig. 13), and even in crystal growth (Fig. 14) although in the last case the basic mechanism is given an overall symmetry. All these branching structures start from a point and grow lineally, but they eventually stop as the branches interfere with others already present. Until the structure encounters some extraneous obstacle (Fig. 15), the shapes are quite different from the interface-determined shapes discussed above. The structure is that of an individual, not of an aggregate.

There are other structures in which a branched tree-like structure arises from an inverse mechanism. The best known example is the successive joining of many small streams to form a single large river. In brittle solids the merging together of many small cracks to form a single surface gives rise to a similar form (Fig. 16).

The Role of History in Structure

In the typical process amenable to study by physics, the small number of units involved and the simplicity of their interactions gives a definiteness and reproducibility that is either invariant or is dependent in a simple way upon time. In other sciences such as biology or metallurgy, the structure of complex matter must be dealt with, involving myriads of units and interacting interactions, with associations of perfection and imperfection which can be combined in an almost infinite variety of ways. The structures which merit particular study because they happen to exist depend almost completely on their history—quite as much as does, though with more diversity, the present human condition. Although other structures might have been formed with equal a priori probability from the same units and unit processes, the whole unique sequence of atomic-scale events that actually did occur, each adding a little to a pre-existing structure, was necessary to give rise to the particular array of molecules, crystals, or cells in the final structure.* Although the ideal crystal lattice of a substance at equilibrium depends only on its composition and temperature, all other aspects of the structure of a given bit of polycrystalline matter depends upon history, i.e. the details of the nucleation of individual crystals, usually at sites where imperfections or heterogeneities pre-exist in the matrix; the locally varying rates at which the individual crystals grow into their environment, incorporating or rejecting matter as a result of the micro-processes of atom transfer; and the manner in which the crystals impinge to produce the grain boundary as a new element of structure which itself changes shape in accordance with its properties and the particular local geometry all resulting from historical accidents. Far more complex, but in principle similar, things occur in biological and social organizations.

In the space-filling aggregate, the individuals limit each other. They may be arrayed randomly or regularly, but however undetermined the shape of an individual, the conditions of joining at the points where three or more meet are defined. Structure on one level, by its imperfections or variations, always gives rise to a new kind of structure on a larger scale. (Inversely, it may even be that there is no detectable structure without some underlying structure on a smaller scale. The validity of atomism depends on the tool used to find it.) A local configuration will always have some connection to neighboring ones. In ever-decreasing degree every part is dependent on the whole and vice versa.

On Sections and Surfaces

The structures usually observed on metals and rocks are those of a plane section cut through a three-dimensional structure, slicing through the crystal planes and boundaries at various angles, and thus introducing distortions of shape and hiding connections that may exist in the third dimension. We have become very adept at interpreting things from two-dimensional representation, indeed most of our thinking is in such terms. The two-dimensional surface of a painting can represent a straight or distorted projection or a point-perspective view of either real or imaginary things. In sculpture, the surface can be the natural surface of an object, but it is usually a cut through a body of material which has a three-dimensional structure and it reveals a surface texture with its own aesthetic qualities. Sections are

* I am indebted to John R. Platt for pointing out that biology is essentially an historical science. The idea is elaborated by Ludwig von Bertalanffy, *Problems of Life*, New York (1952).

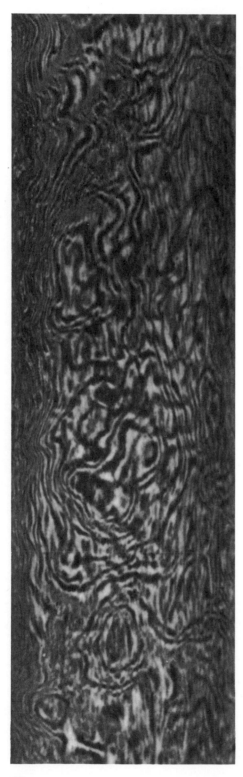

subtly different from the same structures when formed against a real surface—compare Fig. 4 of the real surface of a polycrystalline metal with Fig. 3 of a section: in the former the angles are nearly all at 120°, while the latter has a pleasing diversity. Sectioning is simpler than other two-dimensional representation because there is no superposition as in projection and no change of scale as in perspective: it gives a single-elevation contour map, with volumes reduced to areas, surfaces to lines, and lines to points. If the structure is cellular and randomly oriented, representations of all possible views will be seen at various places in the section. Depending on the orientation, certain features will be magnified in one direction. Convexity or concavity of a surface in relation to the sectioning plane produces closed isolation or extended connectivity of the linear traces on it. If the structure is not random, but irregularly lamellar as the grain of a tree, the variations in the third dimension can be seen as a distribution of texture in the two-dimensional slice. Some examples in which such structures are exploited are wood-veneer textures, marbled ceramics, the Damascus sword (Fig. 17) and Japanese swords and *tsuba* (Fig. 18). These all owe much of their charm to the suggestion of combined design and texture that they display, with effects not unlike those of woven textiles but more natural in origin and with three-dimensional overtones.

Conclusion

Do not these simple structures of crystals and the simpler ones of bubbles graphically illustrate some important features of the world and our appreciation of it, aesthetically as well as intellectually? It is the Chinese principal of *yang* and *yin,* balanced positive and negative deviations from uniformity, which, if occurring at many places must form a foam structure of cells no matter what material-space or idea-space is involved. The freedom of a structural unit inflicts and suffers constraints whenever its closer interaction with some neighbors makes cooperation with others less easy. Social order intensifies the interfacial tension against a differently ordered group. Everything that we can see, everything that we can understand, is related to structure, and, as the *Gestalt* psychologists have so beautifully shown, perception itself is in patterns, not fragments. All awareness or mental activity seems to involve the comparison of a sensed or thought pattern with a pre-existing one, a pattern formed in the brain's physical structure by biological inheritance and the imprint of experience. Could it be that aesthetic enjoyment is the result of the formation of a kind of moiré pattern between a newly sensed experience and the old; between the different parts of a sensed pattern transposed in space and in orientation and with variations in scale and time by the marvelous properties of the brain? The parts of a sensed whole form many patterns suggesting each other in varying scale and aspect, with patterns of imperfection and disorder of one kind forming the partially ordered framework of another with an almost magical diversity depending on the degree to which local deviations from the ideal pattern are averaged out. Somehow the brain perceives the relationship and actively enjoys the rich interplay possible in patterns composed of the simplest parts, an interplay between local and long-range, between branching extension and consolidation, between substance and surface, between order and disorder.

The very nature of life is pattern-matching, whether in the simple acceptance or rejection of "food" units to fit the RNA molecules within a cell or the joining together of conforming and differentiated cells in the overall pattern of the organism which the parts themselves both dictate and conform to. The growth of ordered but lifeless matter typically occurs by the addition of atoms or molecules to the very surface of a crystal. A not dissimilar process of structural matching is involved in the duplication of protein within a living cell, but a complete organism grows by *internal* multiplication, and the consequent burgeoning of outward movement produces the differing environments for cells which is an essential characteristic of a living organism.

There is a kind of indeterminacy (quite different in essence from the famous principle of Heisenberg but just as effective in limiting our knowledge of nature), which lies in the fact that we can neither consciously sense nor think of very much at any one moment. Understanding can only come from a roving viewpoint and sequential changes in the scale of attention. The current precision in science will limit its advance unless a way can be found for relating different but interwoven scales and dimensions.

The elimination of the extraneous, in both experiment and theory, has been the veritable basis of all scientific advance since the seventeenth century, and has led us to a point where practically everything above the atom is understood "in principle". Sooner or later, however, science in its advance will have exhausted the supply of problems that involve only those aspects of nature that can be freshly studied in simple isolation. The great need now is for concern with systems of greater complexity, for methods of dealing with complicated nature as it exists. The artist has long been making meaningful and communicable statements, if not always precise ones, about complex things. If new methods, which will surely owe something to aesthetics, should enable the scientist to move into more complex fields, his area of interest will approach that of the humanist, and science may even once more blend smoothly into the whole range of human activity.

Fig. 17. Detail of a Damascus sword blade from the Wallace Collection, London. The surface of the blade had been formed by cutting through the irregular laminar structure which originated in the crystallization of the high-carbon steel and had maintained its identity during forging. Magnification x 2. *(Photo Courtesy The Wallace Collection, London)*

Fig. 18. A Japanese mokumé swordguard from the collection of G. E. Hearn. The texture arises from the intentional incorporation of innumerable layers of slightly different steels into a single mass by repeated welding and forging, and then chemically etching the final surface which was cut through the forged lamellae. The moon is inlaid in silver. Natural size.

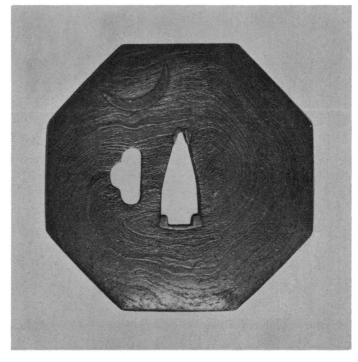

Ever since objects-as-seen were distinguished from objects-in-the-world, men have formulated theories of their relation. A desire to establish semblance, structural equivalence, isomorphism, correspondence, or some other mode of correlation between the presumedly complementary entities is evident in the writings of commentators since ancient times. This theme runs through the development of the science of geometrical optics. It has been influential in guiding research in the anatomy and physiology of the visual receptors and their projections in the brain. And it remains with us in contemporary formulations of the psychology of perception. Great progress has been made in these several sciences and has influenced formulation of the relation between sensed object and its correlate. Yet new explanations seem always to lead to new dilemmas.

Ordinary experience of objects seems to raise no problems. The observer opens his eyes and sees his environment; he shuts them and blots out the view. He walks among objects and gains different perspectives of them. He finds that he can touch most objects that are within reach. He talks to others about these objects and shares expectations concerning them. Such common observations convince us that the familiar world of objects has a continuity in time and space which is independent of our scrutiny. The eyes provide vignettes of this world; different senses make other properties accessible. There seems to be nothing problematic in this description of the observer; one would expect that untutored men throughout the ages have shared it. How then does a need for explanation arise? We shall review some of the historical steps in the evolution of these explanations focusing on their underlying logic in the hope of discovering the source of their inadequacy.

In ancient writings on vision two polar points of view were prevalent. On the one hand, emission theorists regarded the eye itself as the source of rays which explore the world somewhat as the fingers palpate objects. On the other hand, reception theorists have regarded the eye as a receiver of information originating from external objects. The classical theory of reception asserted that multiple eidola (copies) are detached from objects to approach and finally enter the eyes of observers. In this manner, the eye and the Sensorium (perceiving mind) behind the eye gain knowledge of the object. The theory was not without criticism. At least one ancient critic objected to the implication that a similacrum as large as that from a soldier, or even a whole army, could enter the pupil of the eye. When the answer was given that the eidolon shrinks to a size appropriate for entering the pupil as it approaches the eye, several new questions arose. The eidolon from an object placed near to the eye must shrink at a faster rate, since it travels a shorter distance, than an eidolon from a more remote object of the same size. Consequently, the eidolon must know its destination prior to its arrival in order to shrink at the rate appropriate for entering the pupil. Yet even assuming that the shrinkage works properly, how can the eye gain information about the true size of the object and its distance? The shrunken eidola entering the pupil from all objects must be of the same size and carry no hint of the sizes of their original objects.

We may note here two aspects of the theory of eidola which have important implications for later thinking. First, only whole entities were supposed to project eidola. This condition implicitly asserts that the external world is in fact composed of just those entities that are perceived as wholes. What is assumed in this assertion becomes, as we shall see, a central problem many centuries later. Second, any lack of equivalence between object and eidola provokes a type of criticism which recurs throughout the early history of this problem and reflects the idea that semblance should be retained in transmission.

Recognition of the difficulties inherent in the theory of eidola makes more plausible the appeal of the emission theory which seems so absurd to the modern mind. The need for explaining proper size of the perceived object and referral to its place in space is avoided in the emission theory. Just as in touching an object the surface of the hand appears to provide the observer with tactual information that is congruent with the surface of the object, so exploration by visual rays can be assumed to provide the observer with a percept of the object of correct size and location. Both emission and reception theories coexisted, often used in combination by writers on optics, even after physical interpretations of light had become available. We may suspect that the appeal of the emission theory resided precisely in its avoidance, by a *fait accompli*, of the problem raised by the reception theory.

The difficulties raised by the ancient reception theory are analogous to those that plague later versions of the theory. In general terms, the source of difficulty is the following. The observer is assumed to see things in the world because something is conveyed to his eye. The conveyance is constrained by certain factors, such as either pupil size or transmission in straight lines, and the constraints make what is conveyed to the eye different from its source. The Sensorium must then reconstitute a likeness, or else it would appear that the observer's version of the object differs from the true properties of the source. Hereafter, we shall refer to this reconstruction as the *effigy*, in contradistinction to the object, according to the usage of Vasco Ronchi (see notes). The relation between what is in the world to be seen (object) and what is actually seen (effigy) now appears to entail many more contingencies than the mere willingness of the observer to open his eyes and obtain appropriate perspectives. We may assume that the power of the mind to reconstruct the effigy was likened to that involved in dreams or even hallucinations. However, it is precisely at this junction that explanation is required. For to the extent that reconstruction is required, grounds for distinguishing dreams from reconstructions of reality must be provided. And the motive for avoiding reconstruction by maintaining semblance in transmission gains force.

Progress beyond the ancient science of optics awaited the work of Alhazen, the Arab physicist of the tenth and eleventh centuries. In addition to his own observations, he had knowledge of the anatomy of the eye, largely that due to Galen (second century A.D.), and the geometrical optics of Euclid. He synthesized these into a viewpoint which resembles that of modern optics. The extent of Alhazen's break with tradition is suggested by the fact that although known by the thirteenth century to Western thinkers familiar with ancient optics, his writings do not appear to have been understood until at least the sixteenth century.

Alhazen was convinced by the phenomenon we call the afterimage that the eye is not the source of visual rays. If it were, why should a residual effigy remain after the object is removed and even after the eyes are closed? An afterimage is easily produced by staring at a clearly defined object for a minute or so and then transferring one's gaze to a blank area. Alhazen claimed that light, conceived of as a stream of minute particles, is thrown off illuminated objects and is disseminated in all directions in straight lines from each point on the object. Such minuscule "point-eidola" would have no difficulties entering the pupil of the eye. We may conjecture from the absence of the idea, that previous thinkers had balked at having parts of objects cast off eidola. It may have seemed unnatural to them to assume that the copy of a unified entity should be broken up into pieces. If the information coming from an object was decomposed into parts, how could it ever be put together again to re-form the whole? If many of these projected parts,

43

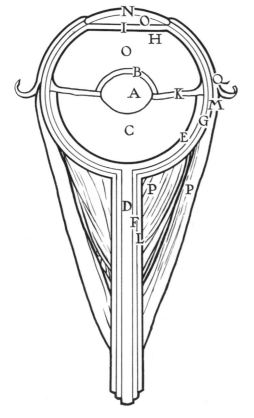

Fig. 1. Diagram representing a section through the axis of the eye and optic nerve. From the first edition of *De corporis humani fabrica* by Andreas Vesalius, 1543. Labeling: A. crystalline lens; B. anterior surface of lens; D. optic nerve; E. retina; I. pupil (which in more accurate representation would not be continuous across the midline); N. cornea. (Reproduced from S. L. Polyak, *The Retina*, Chicago University Press, 1941.)

traveling in lines originating from each point on an object, entered the pupil, they would mix in the eye and confuse the relation of one part to another. The Arab physicist's answer to this dilemma was of that order of ingenuity which forms the permanent tradition of scientific theory.

Alhazen believed the doctrine of Galen which stated that the transparent tunics of the eye consist of concentric spherical layers with the lens of the eye at the center essentially as is shown in Figure 1, drawn five centuries later by Vesalius, the Italian anatomist. Observing that only the projected rays of light entering the eye perpendicularly to the surfaces of the transparent and concentric tunics (the cornea, in particular) would not suffer deviation from their paths by refraction, he attributed to these rays a superior power for exciting vision. They will produce a replicate image of the object according to the following logic. Of all the lines projecting from any point on an object, only one will be perpendicular to the cornea or front surface of the eye. Consequently, from each object point only one effective ray will enter the eye and the set of these rays preserves the topographic structure of their points of origin on the object.

The structured set of rays must of course affect the light-sensitive substance of the eye to produce vision. Any one of the spherical surfaces in the paths of the rays could hypothetically serve as a light-sensitive screen upon which the ordered set of rays would form an image of the object. Which surface should it be? The Galenian tradition said the crystalline lens contained the light-sensitive substance but

Alhazen knew that the crystalline was as transparent as any other internal part of the eye and hence might simply further transmit the light rays. He also knew of the close anatomical relation between the retina and the brain (see Fig. 4) even then regarded as the ultimate seat of sentience. Despite the transparency of the lens, he chose its anterior surface as the light-sensitive surface upon which the image formed. We may presume, together with Vasco Ronchi, that Alhazen did so because he could not accept the conclusion implied by a choice of screen behind the center of the eyeball. The image formed on such a screen would be inverted and reversed with respect to the object, since the straight rays entering the pupil must converge to a point at the center of the eyeball and then diverge. Thus we see that while Alhazen was willing to accept the diminution of size in the relation between image and object implied by the logic of his approach, he balked at the loss of semblance entailed in inversion and reversion of the image.

In answer to the question of how the tiny image formed on the lens could eventuate in an effigy of a size and location coinciding with its object, Alhazen referred to a disposition of the mind to assign the effigy its appropriate size and place. This appeal to what some would today regard as a primitive psychology of vision was required by Alhazen's abandonment of the theory of visual rays which, as we have already discussed, implicitly accounted for the localization of objects in space.

In retrospect, the ancient emission theory of visual rays was a mélange of geometrical, physical, physiological, and psychological concepts. Alhazen demolished that theory. He proposed instead a reception theory that was convincing by virtue of its argument that a replicate image of external objects is formed on the part of the eye supposed to be light-sensitive. By creating a consistent geometrical and physical theory whatever may have been its defects—and some of them were recognized by Alhazen— he was the first in the history of optics to make a clear distinction between the realm of geometrical-physical concepts and what was to become the domain of physiology and psychology. To the latter he assigned the task of reconciling the residual lack of semblance in size and place between effigy and object. In following this mode of reasoning, he anticipated the spirit of the sixteenth century which was to grant the geometrical-physical realm an ontological primacy that relegated appearances to mind. In this process of physicalizing the world, physical properties of objects begin to delimit the demand for semblance between effigy and object. The light-reflecting and light-refracting properties of bodies and the straight line propagation of light rays circumscribe the characteristics of objects which can be identified with effigies precisely because they imply the formation of an image and maintenance of structural resemblance in transmission to the eye. Other characteristics of the effigy may correspond to object properties but no stronger resemblance can be defined.

The medieval attitude toward the use of eyeglasses is a curious chapter in the history of optics and one that clearly bears the mark of the demand for semblance. Eyeglasses are supposed to have been invented toward the end of the thirteenth century and were in common use during succeeding centuries. Yet there is little mention in scientific works of these aids to vision until the sixteenth century. The main reason for this absence appears to be condemnation of their use on theoretical grounds. Since lenses distort the appearances of objects and create illusions, their use can only lead to deception. However mistaken this condemnation appears, it clearly reflects the concern of medieval physicists over maintaining semblance in transmission of information between object and effigy. Before the advantages of eyeglasses could gain a rational understanding, the powers of optical refraction common to both lenses of the eye and lenses of glass would have to be recognized. Only then could inadequacies of the lenses of the eye appear to be correctable by additions of those of glass.

The Italian and Dutch artisans who made eyeglasses also produced the earliest telescopes which were regarded solely as curiosities until copied and used by Galileo at the beginning of the seventeenth century. Galileo inverted the reasoning of the medieval critics of eyeglasses by proclaiming that reality will be better known by the images seen through a telescope than by those seen with the naked eye. In this belief he exhibited the metaphysic behind the movement destined to be called the Scientific Revolution. So much the worse for appearances if they do not lend themselves to mathematical formulation.

Abhorrence of the inverted retinal image was first evident in Alhazen's analysis of vision. It was frequently re-emphasized in the following centuries. Leonardo da Vinci, familiar with the camera obscura (pinhole camera) and the inverted image that it casts on a screen, speaks in his fifteenth-century Notebooks of the eye as the window of the soul. He proposed that a double inversion of light rays occurs within the eye to produce an upright image. Several authors of the sixteenth century, also familiar with the camera obscura, described the fundus or the inside surface of the rear of the eye as a concave mirror which casts an image upon the crystalline lens, thus producing a reinversion of the image. We may presume that these fanciful explanations of image formation were designed to avoid the implication of an inverted image suggested by the analogy of eye and camera obscura. Francisco Maurolycus, writing in the mid-sixteenth century, came very close to Kepler's solution of the problem of image formation by a lens (1604). Maurolycus recognized the crystalline lens of the eye as a true lens and the retina as the surface sensitive to light. However, he also balked at the implied inversion of the image and simply asserted in the face of the evidence that the image was in fact produced upright on the retina. We may suspect that one element in his failure to discover the true manner of image formation was an unwillingness to tolerate the loss of semblance implied by an inverted image on the retina.

It remained for Kepler to discover the true geometrical explanation of image formation. He described how a lens bends the multitude of rays approaching it from a point on one side in such a manner as to converge them all to meet at an approximation to a point on the other side of the lens. The order of object and image points being preserved, an inverted replica is formed of the object (see Fig. 3). In short, the dioptrics of the eye act to form an inverted image in a manner not unlike that of the camera obscura. Kepler accepted the implication of the correct geometrical theory where Maurolycus had apparently refused. So convincing was Kepler's construction that within a few decades almost all mention of competing theories of geometrical optics disappeared. By 1625 Scheiner had verified Kepler's contention by removing the opaque layers at the back of an eyeball and viewing the actual picture formed on the retina as shown in Fig. 3. Kepler was not unaware of the problem of the inverted image which appears to have been such a stumbling block to previous thinkers. However, he relegated its solution to what we would today call physiology or psychology, much as Alhazen had relegated to the mind the projection of the effigy into its place in space some six centuries previously.

One further accompaniment of Kepler's construction deserves mention. If one compares a drawing of the eye made by Vesalius (Fig. 1) before Kepler's publications on optics (1604 and 1611) with a drawing by Scheiner (Fig. 2) made in 1619, one difference is striking. The lens in the latter drawing

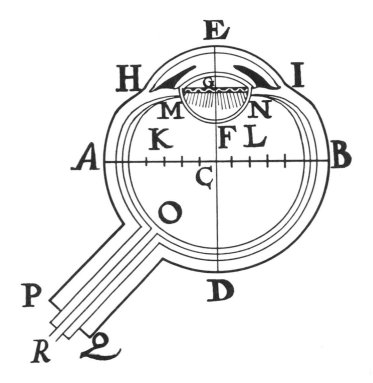

Fig. 2. Section of the eye by Scheiner in *Oculus Hoc Est: Fundamentum Opticum*, 1619. Labeling: C. center of the eyeball; MN. crystalline lens. (Reproduced from S. L. Polyak, *The Retina*, Chicago University Press, 1941.)

has been moved forward to a position more or less identical to that assigned it by modern anatomists. Since Vesalius is known to have practiced dissection, historians of anatomical science have been puzzled by his failure to locate the crystalline lens correctly. We must conclude that it was Kepler's mutation in thought rather than one in anatomy which led Scheiner to the correct representation of the eye. This change required acceptance of the inverted retinal image and consequently of a breach of semblance in transmission from object to effigy. Only the power of Kepler's geometrical explanation of image formation had finally overcome the abhorrence of inversion. But the age of Kepler and Galileo was one in which geometrical demonstration triumphed over intuition and orthodoxy in many areas. We must also recognize that the upright image is relinquished for the gain of a convincing account of image formation in the eye which does, after all, satisfy the demand for structural semblance.

Kepler felt that discussion of the fate of the image beyond the retina was not in his province. But already in ancient times, the assertion appears that the brain is the ultimate seat of sentience—for our purposes the place in which incoming information is transformed to the effigy. To reach the brain from the crystalline lens, visual spirits, variously defined, were assumed to flow between brain and lens carrying the replica. This conception provoked no particular problem since it was designed to insure semblance. With the advent, however, of a more physicalistic approach to bodily function new problems arose over correspondence.

Descartes was apparently the first to feel the need for a more explicit theory of transmission of visual information beyond the retina. In an amazing anticipation of a theory still maintained, he speculated about a point-to-point projection of light-activated portions of the retina upon higher centers of the brain (Fig. 4). It is not surprising that Descartes should have been among the first to deal with the problem in this fashion. As an answer to the very general problem of comprehending the role of Mind in a universe regarded according to Whitehead as one in which "the course of nature is conceived as being merely the fortunes of matter in its adventure through space", Descartes proposed his radical dualism. All bodily function was mechanical, contact of the unextended soul with the body-machine occurred at the pineal body (see Fig. 4). From the present point of view, Descartes' proposal removed sentience to a point deep within the brain in response to a faith in the power of the new geometrized physics to explain the workings of the animate body as well as the inanimate universe. The optic nerve and more central parts of the brain are now conceived as a physical medium of transmission imposing its own constraints upon what is transmitted.

Within the domain of the nervous system, the program of Descartes gained scientific content through the work of anatomists and physiologists of the seventeenth, eighteenth, and nineteenth centuries. The establishment first of the principle of irritability in muscle by Glisson and Swammerdam and later of conduction in nerve by Haller led in the eighteenth century to the conclusion that nerves transmit information by virtue of their own intrinsic powers. For purposes of transmission, this conclusion was analogous to the physical interpretation of light reached in optics many centuries before. The preservation of structural semblance must now be in terms not merely of properties of light, but behind the retina transmission must be in terms of conducting properties of nerve. In the nineteenth century, anatomical studies of the fine structures of the visual nervous system led to the concept of a "cortical retina". This notion gave content to the Cartesian idea of a point-to-point projection from retina to cerebral cortex. Granting its validity, the cortical retina provides a neural replica of the retinal image and carries semblance, now defined as a set of corresponding points preserving topographic order, deep inside the brain. Against this viewpoint, claims of a more diffuse projection from retina to brain were maintained. Such claims appear always to have evoked the opposition of orthodox anatomists who tend to look for order in anatomical connections. But if we question why the particular order was sought in the visual nervous system, the motive again appears to be preservation of semblance. Before a more diffuse projection from retina to cortex could be acceptable, a new principle of ordering for correspondence would have to be made available. A problem analogous to that faced both by Alhazen and Kepler has recurred.

By the nineteenth century, a new discipline arose and called itself psychophysics. Its founders were the German physiologists E. H. Weber and G. T. Fechner, and its greatest exponent was Hermann v. Helmholtz. This discipline was heavily dependent upon the physics and physiology of its day. Its programmatic basis derived from contemporary concepts of nervous structure: principally the idea of encoding sensory excitation into neural messages transmitted to higher centers in the brain. Psychophysical research was directed at finding the minimal detectable differences between stimulations applied to the separate senses. Detection of such differences was thought tantamount to discovering the properties of nerves and the distribution of their fibers. The visual effigy, or percept as it now became called, was to be constructed from information brought by nerve fibers to higher brain centers. The doctrine of specific nerve energies, proposed by the German physiologist Johannes Müller in 1826, was a step in this direction. For Müller excitation of the nerve of any one of the five principal senses resulted in the sensed quality

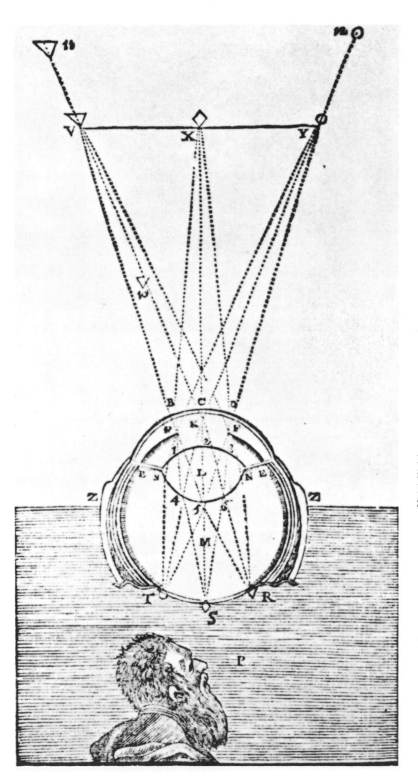

Fig. 3. Diagram explaining the course of the rays of light in the eye and the formation of the image on the retina. From Descartes, *La Dioptrique*, 1637. (Reproduced from S. L. Polyak, *The Retina*, Chicago University Press, 1941.)

specific to that nerve, e.g. sound for stimulation of the auditory nerve, sight for the optic nerve and so on. Helmholtz and others extended this notion to different qualities within separate senses.

The doctrine of specific nerve energies really formalized what was already implicit in earlier ideas of correspondence as opposed to semblance. With progressive scientific knowledge of the media of transmission, semblance must give way to correspondence. The properties of effigies resemble neither their objects of origin nor any physically conceivable media of transmission. The connection of effigy with object of origin becomes construed as a set of one-to-one translations of object properties into those of transmission and finally into qualities of the senses. Just as the mind may apparently create an effigy as in a dream, so the nerves when excited, by whatever cause, create the sensed quality specific to them. Normally, correspondence enforces the distinction between appropriate and non-appropriate excitation of the nerves.

The effigies of vision—our particular concern—were supposed by the nineteenth-century psychophysiologists to be constructed out of many separate and distinct excitations each either bearing or acquiring the mark of its origin on the retina, called a local sign. This information was available to the brain in the form of discrete elements. Construction of the effigy was at first conceived solely as an additive process. But observations of the apparent non-additivity of the elements destined to form the effigy raised new difficulties. For example, the familiar visual-spatial illusions show that lines of equal lengths, objectively defined, cannot be assumed to yield equal perceived lengths. The so-called constancies of visual space are another case in point. A circular plate appears circular even when it is tilted and projects an ellipse on the retina. We are all familiar with the difficulty the untrained have with drawing in perspective. Both ends of a water glass are inevitably drawn as circles by children because they are seen as circular. In the case of constancies, the brain somehow manages to construct the expected effigy despite losses of simple correspondence in transmission. In the case of illusions the constructions are perversely incorrect. There were many attempts to get around these difficulties but the most interesting from our point of view has been that of the *Gestalt* psychologists.

Partly in recognition of the unsolved problems of correspondence this group of German psychologists proposed in the early decades of this century that the brain has autonomous constructive processes that effect nonadditive solutions. The central processes were assumed to be just those that will, in general, reconstruct the appropriate effigies. These effigies will, in turn, correspond with objects in the world.

Wolfgang Köhler has developed an ingenious theory of electroionic fields in the brain designed to have properties isomorphic with certain characteristics of what we have termed effigies. Isomorphism (similarity of structure) can be regarded as a particular version of semblance. However compelling have been these arguments, they have not convincingly demonstrated that the autonomous processes will perform the appropriate reconstruction. As a consequence recent writers, such as J. J. Gibson, have pointed out that *gestalt* theories of organization don't really explain what we have called the correspondence between object and effigy. And in an attempt to outflank the problem of reconstruction Gibson has inverted the traditional psychological approach to perception in what he has termed a global psychophysics.

Gibson shares with other modern psychologists of perception a program of investigation which attempts to discern the physical correlates of visual percepts by an analysis of stimulus information coming from the environment. Eschewing the traditional psychophysical assumptions about the elements of neural transmission and their stimuli, some of these adherents of the new psychophysics appeal to complex and higher-order sets of stimuli in the hope of finding the object-effigy correspondence which has eluded older approaches. The complex stimuli include gradients of texture, ratios of stimulus energies, rates of change, and higher derivatives of change in parameters of stimuli. In effect, these authors believe that the object-effigy correspondence must and can be demonstrated; failure to do so without invoking complicated internal constructions has resulted from too limited accounts of the information in stimulation coming from objects. For example, the insistence on point-for-point translation of retinal excitation into sensed quality resulted in the need for construction when the perceptions of complex visual fields did not correspond to the summation of the sensed qualities. If instead, attention is focused on the plethora of stimulation that can be compounded by a higher-order analysis, the correlates of all sorts of properties of the effigy may be discovered. And consequently, the traditional need for construction may be obviated.

Advocates of the new psychophysics have made well-taken criticisms and some interesting discoveries. But the weakness of their approach lies precisely in opening the door to an unlimited set of stimulating conditions without providing a rational principle for selecting from this set likely candidates for correspondence. A research program based on this approach will inevitably be piecemeal and dependent upon hunches of the experimenter. In the older psychophysical approach, restriction of relevant stimulation to that which is simply derived from the object made construction of the effigy problematic. In the new approach, the assumption that the effigy must correspond to some to-be-discovered complex of stimulation makes recovery of the object problematic. The aim of defining organizational processes has been replaced by the equally elusive goal of defining principles of selection.

The history of geometrical optics showed us that preservation of some sort of order among stimuli coming from the environment to the eye was thought essential for correct vision. The retinal image satisfied that demand. It provides not only a point-for-point correspondence with its object but also the topographic arrangement of points is preserved. The latter may be altered without changing the former by the use of optical devices that distort the image. The immediate effect is a perceived distortion of the type so abhorred by the medieval critics of eyeglasses. However, ironically enough for those critics, the perceived distortions lessen during prolonged wearing of such optical devices. The earliest demonstration of this fact appears to be that of Wilhelm Wundt, often regarded as the founder of experimental psychology, in the late nineteenth century. Wundt observed that the apparent curvature of straight lines viewed through a wedge prism diminishes with time. Actually, this finding might have been predicted from the fact that the dioptrics of the eye are far from perfect. Indeed, no less an authority than Helmholtz said of the eye, in one of his Popular Scientific Lectures, that ". . . if an optician wanted to sell me an instrument which had all these defects, I should think myself quite justified in blaming his carelessness in the strongest terms, and giving him back his instrument." Among other aberrations, the lens systems of most eyes have some prismatic power and hence induce curvature of straight lines in certain orientations. Yet these curvatures are rarely, if ever, noticed. It would appear that distortions of this type are eliminated by some natural process whose operation will also compensate for the distortions of the retinal image produced by externally imposed optical devices.

Research in my own laboratory on the process of compensation has shown that correction of distortions of the retinal image involves much more than mere visual stimulation. In many cases a viewer will compensate for distortion only if he actively moves about in his environment. The same viewer when passively moved, yet experiencing the same visual stimulation, will show no compensation for the perceived distortion. This finding implies that the motor side of the nervous system, as well as the visual projections, are involved in the process of compensation. We have also demonstrated in the laboratory that the original development of some aspects of visually guided behavior requires that young animals actively move about in their environments. These researches imply the existence of rather complex processes in the nervous system which utilize the kind of information provided by movement and its visual consequences in order to develop and maintain spatial vision.

We do not know to what extent the topographic arrangement of points on the retinal image can be optically transformed in relation to its object and still allow of compensation. For example, will a viewer compensate for a scrambled image of the environment? Study of the limits of such compensation will eventually tell us about the nature of the internal process that is responsible for adaptation. There are good reasons for supposing that loss of the one-to-one correspondence of object and image points cannot be compensated. An irrecoverable loss of information occurs. But there seem to be no a priori reasons for denying that any transform of the ordering of these points that preserves the correspondence may be compensated. The tendency to maintain invariance of perception despite the rearranged retinal image represents a constancy of higher order than that of the traditional conception. It suggests that ordering principles operate on the information available in the observer's nervous system so as to prescribe appearances.

Having considered many historical explanations of the relation between object and effigy, we may now try to assess its current status. Let us begin with a brief summary of the logic of past explanations. The distinction between object and effigy began with the development of what we call physical descriptions and laws. Though stated by human observers, such laws were presumed valid in a universe without observers. Because perceived objects in the world appear to be independent of scrutiny by the observer, they were assumed to be correlated with the entities of physics. These physical entities were then conceived as the underlying source of continuity of the perceived world. Since the observer has to be informed of properties of his world in order to act appropriately, it appeared that he must have access to objects. He must be able to identify them and recognize their positions in relation to himself. But visual access to the world is obtained by the causal route involved in transmission of information from physical environment to eye and brain. Access to objects is then somehow related to this transmission. We have traced the vicissitudes of this problem. The early demand for semblance in transmission was replaced by that for correspondence as the physicalization of the media of transmission proceeded. But specific theories of correspondence have all seemed problematic. Why has more progress not been made?

If we consider the more recent theories, we find that implicit assumptions vitiate their explanatory power. For example, the older psychophysical approach appears inadequate because of its assumption about the translation of punctate retinal excitation into localized sensation. The *Gestalt* theory of organization, as made explicit by Köhler, cannot readily account for the invariance of perception under the transforms of rearrangement. Both the *Gestalt* theory and the new psychophysics have failed to take account of the possibility that extra-visual factors may influence correspondence. The implicit assumption

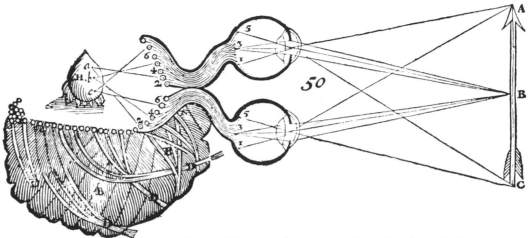

Fig. 4. Diagram of an imagined section through the two eyes, optic nerves, and brain with the point-for-point projections of the retinal images upon the surface of the cerebral ventricles within the brain. The lines of projection are then further extended to the pineal gland (H) where corresponding points from each eye join to form a single representation of the external object (ABC). Among other anatomical inaccuracies, the optic nerves are shown without any fibers crossing the midline to project to opposite sides of the brain. From *Traité de l'homme* by Descartes, published 1686. (Reproduced from S. L. Polyak, *The Retina*, Chicago University Press, 1941.)

that visual percepts are strictly a product of sensory input to the visual nervous system is a relic of the old identification of the visual Sensorium with the projections of the optic nerves in the brain.

We may be able to avoid vitiating assumptions if for a moment we regard the observer with all his capabilities as a machine having unknown rules of operation. Then any and all of its activities and informational input may be relevant to its output. It is immediately evident that if this machine does in fact respond adaptively to physically definable properties of its environment, then information about those properties must be available to the system that controls its behavior. This sort of specification is implicit in all theories of visual correspondence. But what has not always been recognized is that the specification tells us nothing either about the machine's method of processing the information which must be available to it or about the manner in which this information will relate to perceived objects. In short, the familiar objects in the world of an observer need not correspond in any simple way to properties of the environment that control the observer's adapted behavior. As we have seen, too often in the past the transmission of information from the environment to the behaving organism has been confounded with the need to transmit specially ordered information, in the form of eidola or images, from familiar objects to the eye. What sort of an information processing system could conceivably yield the correspondence that is sought? We might as well confront it with the most general and difficult demand that we know of. The system should be capable of the kinds of pattern recognition of which human observers are capable. If the system is capable of this sort of perceptual achievement, it seems safe to assume that it will in principle perform less difficult tasks.

The powers of pattern recognition are nowhere more evident than in recognition of speech and handwriting. Despite the enormous variability in physical properties, recognition of such linguistic entities by an adult familiar with his language is almost instantaneous and rarely in error. We cannot conclude that this ability is acquired through a long period of education during which all the variant forms become associated with the correct response. To some extent every instance of speech or handwriting is unique. For that matter, every instance of a tree, or even of a given perspective of a tree, is unique. The commonly used explanation that similarity of instances is the source of a common response to disparate stimulation simply begs the issue. We are forced to conclude that having been presented with a relatively small sample of instances, the system can recognize an unlimited set. And such constructive power must entail a set of principles of operation intrinsic to the human nervous system.

Linguists, under the leadership of N. Chomsky, have made considerable progress in defining the principles required for use of language. Little progress has been made in this direction for perception in general. Nevertheless, the arguments are convincing that the workings of such principles determine both what information from the environment will be utilized and how it will be classified in the form of perception. Consequently, the identity and continuity of objects can be regarded as the outcome of this processing rather than as its cause. The establishment of correspondence then becomes tantamount to discovering the laws of operation of the perceptive mechanism. This realization does not yield a theory of correspondence but it does indicate a direction of inquiry for resolution of some of the puzzles that previous explanations have provoked.

It is difficult, if not impossible, to cite the many sources of information upon which this paper is based. Readers will surely recognize my debt to many contemporary authors. The list of citations would include at least the following sources of historical information:

E. G. Boring	*Sensation and Perception in the History of Experimental Psychology*, New York, Appleton-Century-Crofts (1942).
F. Fearing	*Reflex Action*, Baltimore, The Williams & Wilkins Co. (1930).
H. Helmholtz	*Popular Scientific Lectures*, New York, Dover Publications (1962).
H. Helmholtz	*Physiological Optics*, New York, Dover Publications (1962).
S. L. Polyak	*The Retina*, Chicago, The University Press (1941).
S. L. Polyak	*The Vertebrate Visual System*, Chicago, The University Press (1957).
V. Ronchi	*Optics, the Science of Vision*, New York, The University Press (1957).
V. Ronchi	*Histoire de la lumière*, Paris, S.E.V.P.E.N. (1956).

I wish to acknowledge my debt to the National Institutes of Mental Health (grant M-07642) for supporting research which led to this account of the problem.

My subject in this essay is the relation between the treatment of natural forms in the art of any one time, and the view of nature which preoccupies the science of the same time. In particular, I want to relate the radical changes which have entered art in this century to the profound change which the logic of science has undergone in the century. In order to set the scene for these comparisons, I will begin by giving illustrations of two different problems which engage the interests of scientists. My illustrations come from mathematics, for no better reason than that I am a mathematician; and they happen to be two of the beautiful unsolved problems in mathematics.

The first problem was proposed by an amateur, Christian Goldbach, to the great Leonhard Euler in 1742, when he had already begun to go blind. The raw material for the problem consists, very simply, of the prime numbers—that is, the numbers 2, 3, 5, 7, 11 and so on, which are distinguished by the fact that none of them can be made up by multiplying two smaller numbers together. Goldbach's conjecture asserts, with deceptive innocence, that every even number is the sum of two prime numbers. For example, the even number 28 is the sum of 17 and 11 (and, incidentally, is also the sum of 23 and 5). Every example that has ever been tested has come out right; but to this day Goldbach's conjecture has never been proved, and we do not know whether it is true.

The second problem was posed (or almost posed) by A. F. Möbius in 1840; it has the distinction that several great mathematicians have at different times believed that they had solved it, but their solutions have always turned out to contain a hidden flaw. The raw material for the problem consists of any flat map, which is divided into different countries. (A country consists of a single area, and two countries are neighbors if they have a boundary in common—the boundary being a finite line of any shape.) The problem is to color the map so that countries which are neighbours are colored differently; and the conjecture is that four colors are always enough to do this. This is the famous Four Color theorem; no map has ever been found on which it fails, but it has not been proved for the general case, and we do not know whether it is true.

These two problems are very different, and the difference is the crux of my argument. Goldbach's hypothesis is a problem in traditional mathematics; by contrast, the Four Color theorem is a problem in modern mathematics. That is, any reader will recognize Goldbach's hypothesis as mathematics; but many readers would not even recognize the Four Color theorem as a mathematical problem. The Four Color theorem does not sound like any problem they were set at school, and does not have the feel of mathematics as they were taught it. The reason is that the two problems lie in different fields: Goldbach's hypothesis is concerned with arithmetic, and the Four Color theorem is concerned with geometry—with a sophisticated geometry (in which the countries may have any shape) which is called topology. Everyone knows that numbers are mathematics; but odd geometrical shapes, the topological arrangement of a map, are not mathematics for the common reader. They do not have the sort of exactness which he has been taught to expect of mathematics and of science.

The common reader is accustomed to think of science as the pursuit of facts; and the more exact the facts, the more scientific he feels them to be. This is the picture of science which was created in the public mind by the researchers of the last century. It was put into words most pointedly by one of the giants of mathematical physics in that age, Lord Kelvin, in two sentences which are still quoted as gospel.

"If you can measure that of which you speak, and can express it by a number, you know something of your subject. If you cannot measure it, your knowledge is meagre and unsatisfactory."

That was a hundred years ago: science then was the manipulation of exact measurements. Now, in the twentieth century, the stress has shifted. Measurement and precision are still necessary, of course, but we now recognize them to give only the raw material for science. The aim of science, we now see, is to find the relations which give order to this raw material, the shapes and structures into which the measurements fit. We are no longer preoccupied with the mere facts, but with the relations which the facts have with one another—with the whole which they form and fill, not with the parts. In place of the arithmetic of nature, we now look for her geometry: the architecture of nature.

Of course ours is not the first age to be inspired by the geometry of nature. The Greeks thought in this way, and the books of Euclid remain as a monument to the excitement with which they pursued the search for logical form and natural form. It happens that we know the Greek outlook best in its mathematical expression, because by chance the books of Euclid became first a classic and then a school primer. But this outlook, the belief that the logic of nature expresses itself in the arrangement of her geometrical shapes, reached into every part of Greek thought. In art, it caused the Greeks to think more, and more highly, of sculpture and of architecture than of painting. In physics, it made them identify the atoms of their four elements, fire, air, water and earth, with four of the classical regular solids. They got over the embarrassing fact that there is a fifth regular solid by identifying it with the hidden essence of nature, which we obediently still call the quintessence.

When the Renaissance recovered many Greek writings on art and on mathematics, it naturally took over the Greek view. The immediate example is the hoard of material which Leonardo da Vinci heaped up in his notebooks. The notebooks touch on every Renaissance subject, from aerial perspective to the path of the sun, and from the flight of birds to the casting of statues. Yet two subjects dominate them, and dominate Leonardo's mind. One is the internal mechanism of machines: wheels, pulleys, gears, ratchets, and arrangements which make a machine carry out a sequence of operations, step by step, automatically. The other is structural anatomy: the coordinated arrangement of bones and muscles which enables the animal body to move and act as a unity.

These two overriding interests of Leonardo's are two facets of a single outlook. As his paintings show, he is looking for the bone beneath the skin, the articulated skeleton which supports and directs the fleshy covering. Renaissance painting found several devices to give solidity to the flat picture: for example, geometrical perspective was such a device. But the outstanding discovery was that which tumbles and spills through every page of Leonardo's notebooks: the discovery of structure by burrowing under the surface of nature, and entering the outer form from within. Leonardo in painting, Verrocchio in sculpture, and many others, were discovering the machine in the human and animal frame.

We make the word "machine" sound derogatory nowadays, but we must not let this usage color our respect for the cardinal discovery of the Renaissance artists. They painted the human body vigorously and solidly because they had learned how it works: what ropes pull on the bones and what joints hinge one bone to another. Leonardo in particular was fascinated by the automatic coordination of the parts of the body, by which the movement of a single finger is integrated into an organized and total gesture. And it is characteristic that this is also the theme of most of the machines which he invented and drew. They are nearly all automatic machines: automatic lathes, file cutters, gear cutters, an automatic feed to a spinning-frame or to a printing-press. Leonardo is occupied with the logic of the processes he sees, in men and machines, and he looks for the hidden structure because it expresses that logic. If he were working now, when the mechanics of the body are understood, he would be looking for the logical sequence of the processes in the brain; and he would be studying it, as some biologists are doing now, by analyzing the functioning of electronic machines.

I must not leave the Renaissance without stressing what is constantly forgotten, that Leonardo was not unique in his outlook. He was more lucid, more outspoken, more vocal than other artists—if I can use the word "vocal" to describe his drawing in his notebooks, which constitutes an unwritten language to express whatever came into his head. But the interest in perspective, in logical design, and particularly in anatomy, was universal. For example, one of the two classics of science which were published in 1543 (the other was by Copernicus) was the book of anatomical drawings by Andreas Vesalius, *De Humani Corporis Fabrica*. The human body in the work of Vesalius, the horses of Leonardo, are no more alive or evocative than, say, the race-horses and their jockeys that Edgar Degas painted in the nineteenth century. But they have an inner strength, a grace made out of efficiency, which is missing in the colored movement of Degas; they are tense as machines wound up for the race.

There was a major shift in outlook some time after the age of Leonardo and Vesalius. The change did not come all at once; it accumulated through the seventeenth and eighteenth centuries, until by the nineteenth century it had become the established habit of science. The search for physical mechanisms below the surface of nature gradually fell back. The interest in isolated detail grew. Science came to be admired as the Puritan guardian of literal truth, whose aim it was to describe the material world visibly to the last decimal point. Exact measurement became an end in itself, until it seemed to carry an almost moral sense of undeviating righteousness. One effect of this, which is still with us, was to make the scientist seem inhuman, a pedant out of science fiction (Phileas Fogg as Jules Verne pictures him), and to put him apart from the sad, merry, sloppy, glamorous hotchpotch of life as lived by the artists in *La Bohème*.

I cannot put my finger on the moment when this transformation began. And I ought to say that, when it began, it was indeed necessary to the progress of science. When Galileo and Isaac Newton in the seventeenth century laid fresh foundations for the physical sciences, the chief obstacle that impeded them was the heritage of vague general laws and *a priori* theories which were still traditional in science. They had to get rid of the crystal spheres, and perfect motion, and of ill-defined laws which announced, with anthropomorphic solemnity, that "nature abhors a vacuum" and *"ex nihilo nihil fit"*. The pioneers in the seventeenth century had to insist that the laws and concepts of science must be capable of exact meaning and of rigorous empirical test in detail.

All this was necessary in Newton's time as a new method—and a method which lucid observers like Leonardo and Vesalius had helped to prepare. But somehow, from the eighteenth century, the new empirical method became a fetish, an addiction to observation in itself and for its own sake. Perhaps the overpowering reputation of Newton, morose, absorbed, and impatient of argument, had something to do with this. "I do not make hypotheses" he had said, rightly in his day; and the dictum stifled speculation for two hundred years. Perhaps the mathematical system that he uncovered in nature was too impressive; no other kind of system found much foothold, roughly until Charles Darwin proposed the more erratic and unpredictable machinery of evolution in 1859. For two hundred years, Newton's laws were accepted as the model to which all nature conforms, and which had been discovered once for all; and science became the meticulous description of the surface phenomena of this everlasting world.

Perhaps I am wrong to make Newton the cause and symbol of this narrow and over-empirical view of science. Perhaps all this was in the air by 1660, with or without Newton. For example, in that year in Holland there were alive and active Spinoza, Anthony Van Leeuwenhoek, Rembrandt and Christian Huygens. Spinoza was earning his living by grinding lenses, and Leeuwenhoek in his amateur way was making even stronger lenses, in order to study microscopic animals. They were caught up in an intense interest in the phenomena of light which also transformed the art of painting in Rembrandt and the science of optics in Huygens. The intellectual life of Holland and (through Huygens) of France was suffused with an excited interest in the play and the behavior of light. In the same decade falls the year 1666, in which the young Newton discovered the law of gravitation, and of which he wrote in old age nostalgically that then "I was in the prime of my age for invention." Indeed he was, for he also recalled that when he went to Stowbridge Fair "in the year 1666, I procured me a triangular glass prism to try therewith the celebrated Phenomena of Colours." Newton's beautiful work in analyzing the spectrum began in that year.

The attention to light, and particularly to the colors of the spectrum, went far beyond the circle of scientists in the newly founded Royal Society in England and Académie Royale in France. It made it natural for the poets of the eighteenth century to use color-words many times more profusely than either Chaucer or François Villon or even Shakespeare had used them. It brightened and varied the palette of Dutch and English painters. And it also shifted their interest from the solid form to the surface, from the structure to the appearance. The tradition of painting with light begins then, and goes on to dominate art to the end of the nineteenth century, in the work of William Turner in England and the Impressionists in France. For all of them, the truth of nature was the truth of the appearance; in the Impressionists, for example, it became the minute detail of light which played over and revealed the stretched skin of the surface.

We can date the change in the outlook of science at the turn of the nineteenth century quite closely. One landmark was the discovery of X-rays by Wilhelm Röntgen in 1895. The other was the series of findings which turned the abstract concept of the atom into a concrete physical entity. These findings began, perhaps, from the work (inspired, oddly, by the ideas of Darwin) by James Clerk Maxwell in England and Ludwig Boltzmann in Germany on the statistical behavior of large assemblies of atoms. They reached their climax in the demonstration by Max von Laue and his followers from 1912 onwards that the atoms in a crystal are arranged in regular patterns.

The impact of the discovery of X-rays is obvious, and was immediate. Suddenly there was given to man an instrument which did without effort what the genius of Leonardo and Vesalius had labored to do—which saw, literally, the skull beneath the skin and the bone within the flesh. The discovery interested everyone, and it changed the taste of a generation. From that moment, the upholstered forms of Victorian furniture and Victorian women were on their way out, and the stark and spiky fashions of the twentieth century began. We can see the hand of Röntgen reaching out still to shape the metal of sculptors today.

But the revelations of X-rays did not go far enough. What they saw was, after all, only what the Renaissance painters had already uncovered, the skeleton. This was certainly a structure, but it was a known structure: its mechanism was still that of the ball and socket and the universal joint. The decisive step of our century was to penetrate beyond the mechanical scale of structure down to the atomic scale.

Structure is both a logical and an architectural conception: the recognition of an order among individual pieces in which the pieces are illuminated by their total arrangement. In the Renaissance vision, the pieces still had functions in themselves; they were not mere featureless units. In the vision of our age, von Laue's vision, the units are atoms, which are as indistinguishable as the bricks in a building. The pieces have lost (or almost lost) their own meaning, and the structural or logical pattern is in complete command.

This has become the fruitful approach in every field of science today. We study in crystals not what they are made of, but how they are put together; our study is directed by the fundamental fact of geometry, that space has only seven forms of symmetry. The crystals of metals have only three forms, which give them their special properties. One of the first men to guess at this way of thinking was August Kékule, who had the idea in 1858 that six atoms of carbon might arrange themselves in a closed ring. He could not foresee that a hundred years later, it would seem obvious to us that the alignment of the rings would determine the properties of solid carbon. If these rings are laid flat, one above the other, they will make graphite, which is soft because they slide. But if the rings are interlocked, they will make diamond, which is hard because they cannot move.

In this way, there has been opened to our century a vision of the fine structure of nature which is different from that of the Renaissance because it is no longer visible: its forms bear no obvious relation to natural shapes. The search in the arts for new forms which lie deeper than the skeleton seems to me to express the same vision. Cubism was a first step in this, which tried to organize body and landscape under a single form. It is not obvious that the atoms in a crystal of common salt ought to lie at the corners of a lattice of cubes; yet this is what Lawrence Bragg (inspired by von Laue) discovered in Cambridge in 1913. And it is not obvious that the cube might be an element of structure which is universally evocative, as Pablo Picasso had suddenly thought in a village on the Ebro four or five years earlier.

We have learned a great deal more about atomic structure in the fifty years since then. We have come to understand why less tidy materials, such as rubber and wool, stretch and curl. We have learned that a sulfa drug is effective because the geometrical arrangement of its atoms causes bacteria to mistake it for the body chemical on which they feed. We understand why the viruses form themselves into crystals which have the unexpected shapes of some of the classical regular solids of Greece. We have elucidated the geometrical shape of living molecules which endows them with the basic property of life—to divide and then to build on each half an identical copy of the original whole. And we have even begun to decipher the orderly code in which the atoms of a living molecule arrange themselves to pass on the message of heredity from one generation to the next. The message is precise, yet the secret of the code is not in the arithmetic—it is in the arrangement, the geometry.

This is the outlook of modern science: a search, not for numerical measurements, but for topological relations as odd as the Four Color theorem and the invented spaces of Möbius. The public is hardly aware of the change in science to these new and revolutionary concepts of logical structure. Yet it seems to me that artists have been sensitive to this intellectual change, and have reflected it in their work quite as vividly as scientists have. I find it in much abstract painting, in the search for significant structure which shall be neither mechanical nor biological, and in the topological forms to which modern sculpture has refined the traditional nude.

I will close with a single example, when I ought to give many; it will serve as a pithy and concrete illustration. My example is the sculpture of Henry Moore, which I greatly admire. The shapes which Henry Moore gives to the human form are strong and highly organized, but they are not organized on the frame of the skeleton (Figs. 1-3). He is saying something else about the body than that it has bones in it; he is saying that the limbs are connected by a geometry which is characteristically human and (in his nudes of women) feminine. The shapes that he makes owe their humanity to their characteristic topology.

The forms of Henry Moore in sculpture are so strong that it is a surprise to see his drawings for them, or the famous drawings of sleepers in underground shelters made during the air raids on London in the 1940's (Figs. 4-5). In these drawings, the form is created by an accumulation of small nervous lines scribbled one over the other. The solid figure is there, but it is reached by a strangely tentative process which is the opposite of the strong outline of Leonardo or Auguste Rodin. To my mind, this way of drawing for sculpture is characteristic of our sense, today, that the structures which lie under the natural forms are minute, and unrelated to the visible outline. The strong shape is filled and organized by invisible linkages of atoms.

For fifty years we have been living in an intellectual revolution, in which interest has shifted from the surface appearance to the underlying structure, and then from the gross structure to the fine organization of minute parts in which only the total pattern expresses an order. And while critics have argued who has the monopoly of the new vision, and which culture ought to scorn the other, artists and scientists have gone quietly about their business of feeling and expressing the same common revolution.

Fig. 1. Henry Moore. *Four-Piece Composition: Reclining Figure,* 1934. Private collection.

Fig. 3. Henry Moore. *The Bride*, 1940. Museum of Modern Art, New York. Lillie P. Bliss Bequest.

Fig. 2. Henry Moore. *Reclining Figure*, 1939. Collection Sir Kenneth Clark.

Fig. 4. Henry Moore. *Studies for Sculpture*, 1948. Private collection.

Fig. 5. Henry Moore. *Pale Shelter Scene*. Reproduced by Courtesy of the Trustees of the Tate Gallery, London.

R. BUCKMINSTER FULLER

CONCEPTUALITY OF FUNDAMENTAL STRUCTURES

What do we mean by the word structure? I have pondered on it a great deal and have decided to define "structure" literally from a descriptive consideration of its natural occurrence—for instance, its occurrence in chemical elements—for the family of chemical elements and their most complex agglomerations as super star galaxies are alike fundamental structures. It is clear in the results of modern scientific experiment that structures are not *things*.

We might define structures descriptively as *patterns of inherently regenerative constellar association of energy events*. That sounds intricate and obscure at first so perhaps I had better explain what I mean by each of the terms. For instance by *inherent* I mean behavior *principles* discovered by man always to be reliably operative in universe under a given set of circumstances. I use the term *regenerative* because in an all-motion universe (which Einstein posited and the physicists in due course found to hold true), all the patterns of the universe are continually but non-simultaneously affecting all the other patterns of universe in varying degrees and are continually reduplicating themselves in unique local configurations. These patterns (Fig. 1) may be described as *constellar* because their component events stand dynamically together like star groupings, and any event patternings which become locally regenerative are constellar patterns. It is a tendency of patterns either to repeat themselves locally or for their parts to separate-out to join severally or singly with other patterns or to form new constellations.

All the forces operative in universe result in a complex progression of most comfortable (i.e. least effort) arrangements in which the macro-medio-micro star events stand together here and there as locally regenerative patterns. I call these spontaneously regenerative local constellations basic structures since they appear to be universally and inherently recurrent. This definition of structure holds true all the way from whole non-simultaneous universe through all the lesser local and inherently regenerative pattern differentiations down to the atom and its nuclear subassemblies.

It is interesting in considering the meaning of structure, to think of the redefinitions emerging annually at the Massachusetts Institute of Technology in respect to fundamental phenomena. Every February the Institute exhibits, in the main entry hall on Massachusetts Avenue, a collection of self-definitions by the various academic departments. This is done so that the prospective students for the coming year (it is enrollment time at mid-years) may consider what the Institute has to offer. The Physics Department, the Chemistry Department, the Mathematics Department and so on,

all make statements about their particular concerns. They must say what they have to offer to the prospective students in a way that is both comprehensible and of high integrity of scientific meaning. Casual suggestions of the nature of the work will not suffice. Thus, annually each department has found it necessary to re-examine its inexorably evoluting disciplines and where appropriate to redefine its subject. Since each year both man's art and science of communication have improved, I have found it interesting to note how for instance the Physics Department at the Massachusetts Institute of Technology redefines itself as the years go on.

There has been such a rapid evolution in the sciences that what for instance the Physics Department said it was concerned with in 1912 was not what it professed in 1922. In 1912 (before M.I.T. moved to the Charles River in Cambridge) it was concerned with *mechanics* in general, optics, and so forth, and a phenomenon called electricity was newly included as an appendix. By 1922 science was overwhelmed with the newly discovered world of electron behaviors and the Physics Department said publicly that physics was primarily concerned with electronics. Physics in 1950 at the same Institute was described as being concerned almost entirely with the nucleus of the atom.

Fig. 1. Four non-simultaneous rocket bursts with visually overlapping patterns. Their four stars constitute the four vertices of a tetrahedron—the fundamental quantum of universe's structuring. There is a tetrahedronal structural *interrelationship* between (1) *the day before yesterday,* (2) *yesterday,* (3) *today,* and (4) *tomorrow.* Though we speak of them as "the four balls in the air"—maintained there successively by a juggler using five balls to do his trick—they are not the same balls and the four are never in the same positions; nonetheless there are always, and only, six fundamental interrelationships between "the four balls in the air", i.e., ab, ac, ad, bc, bd, cd; a, b, c, d, are non-simultaneous events. Universe structures most frequently consist of the physical *interrelationship* of *non-simultaneous events.* Because of the fundamental non-simultaneity of universal structuring, a single, simultaneous, static model of universe is inherently both "nonexistent", conceptually impossible", as well as "unnecessary". Ergo, *universe does not have a shape.* Do not waste your time, as man has been doing for ages, trying to think of a unit shape "outside of which there must be something", or "within which, at center, there must be a smaller something". All the words in the dictionary do not make one sentence; all the words cannot be simultaneously considered, *yet* each of the words is valid as a tool of communication; and some words combine in a structure of meaning.

The Department of Mathematics at M.I.T. which embraces the fundamental communication systems of all the sciences, is also the most generalized of scientific disciplines. The last time I wrote down its annual statement of self-definition was in 1953. This definition hasn't altered much since then. Mathematics, which is both the most comprehensive and abstract of the sciences, tends to evolve less rapidly than physics or chemistry. Mathematics generalizes all sciences and all other sciences must use it.

M.I.T.'s Department of Mathematics' self definition of 1953 said: "Mathematics, which most people think of as the science of number, is, in fact, *the science of structure and pattern in general*." It went on, for another hundred words or so, but that was the opening sentence. This definition of mathematics as "the science of structure and pattern in general" agrees comfortably with my definition of the word "structure"—structure is not a "thing"—it is not "solid."

Now you know what I mean by structures as the inherently regenerative local constellar subpatternings of universe. Since by my own definition *universe is the historically synchronous aggregate of all men's consciously apprehended and communicated* (to self or others) *experiences* and since the experiences are each finite but non-simultaneous, universe is a non-simultaneous yet dynamically synchronous structure, which is unitarily non-conceptual as of any one moment, yet as an aggregate of finites is sum totally finite. Thus we realize that finite structures are mostly non-conceptual in any momentary sense though certain local structures in universe are momentarily conceptual such for instance as the continually transforming historical aggregate of men's experiences packaged together in the words "planet earth." This may be a difficult introduction to the subject of structures but it sets the stage for further thought searching on a subject whose heretofore illusory "static solidness" has completely misled human thought and occasioned the last century's discoveries of science to be perversely surprising information seemingly to be dealt with only by geniuses.

Let us see how our definition of structure applies to architecture. I often hear it said in our technical schools, and by the public, that architects build buildings out of materials. I point out to architectural students that they do not do that at all. That kind of definition dates back to the era of men's thinking of matter as solid. I tell architectural students that what they do is to organize the assemblage of *visible modular structures out of subvisible modular structures*. Nature itself, at the chemical level, does the prime structuring. If the patterning attempted by the architect is not inherently associative within

the local regenerative dynamics of chemical structure, his buildings will collapse. The kinds of spans man builds, the sizes of his columns, and the ways in which, in the end, man must enclose space, are governed by the fundamental principles of structuring preconceived in a priori structuring laws of nature. The principles governing structure not only prescribe what man can put together, but they are operative at the molecular level, at the atomic level and at the nuclear level. They are also operative in each of man's life cells and throughout principles of structure in the starry heavens. They are universal, they are purely mathematical, weightless.

Now, in order to understand universal structure one must consider the fundamental coordinating system employed by nature. It occurred to me a half century ago that nature might have a coordinating system of her own—which might not be the same system as that which man has arbitrarily invented, adopted and applied to his measuring of nature. It also occurred to me that nature probably did not have separate departments of physics, chemistry, biology, mathematics and sociology, etc. In formulating the quadrillions of bubbles per second in the waters of Niagara Falls, nature has no time in which to refer her structural formulation decisions to bureaucratic conventions of department heads of academic categorical states.

To implement the invention of the calculus, man has used the XYZ coordinate system formalized by Descartes out of the Greek's 90 degree symmetrical cross "tree" of three supposedly straight and supposedly continuous "infinite lines." We have learned to reason only in terms of these experimentally demonstrated fallacial suppositions and only in three dimensions: of width (X), breadth (Y), and depth (Z). But width, breadth and depth do not include consideration of how hot a local structural event may be nor how long it has been there nor how much it weighs. There are a lot of other aspects of Nature which the ghostly Greek kind of geometry did not accommodate, as for instance, the experimental information that two actions cannot take place through the same point at the same time—i.e. two lines cannot run simultaneously through the same point. In the Greek's three-dimensional conceptionings, 90 degree perpendicularity and non-parallelism to a plane already established were essential to qualification as a new dimension. Thus in the development of the XYZ coordinate system, we have found only three unique 90 degree line convergences in a common "point." All our analytical geometry, and the technically difficult structures we build with it, are translated through the XYZ coordinate system. The calculus is used to

Fig. 2. Identical radius, spherical agglomerations in closest packing. The comprehensive coordination of nature's most economical, most comfortable structural interrelationships employs 60° *association* and *disassociation,* which provides an omni-rational interrelationship accounting system—which if arbitrarily accounted on a 90° "three-dimensional basis" becomes inherently irrational.

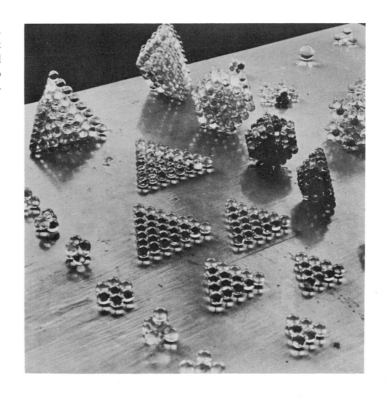

Fig. 3. Vector equilibrium, i.e., a structural system in which the radial vectors and the circumferential vectors are of equal magnitude; ergo the tendency to *explode* or to *contract* is in equilibrium; either *could* but neither *does,* unless something is added or subtracted to change the dynamic balance. Equilibrium is a "dangerous" condition because—due to entropy—something is always about to be added or subtracted to change the balance. When an airplane *stalls* it is in equilibrium. The vector equilibrium consists of four symmetrically interdisposed planes. These four planes are parallel to the four unique, symmetrically interdisposed planes of the regular tetrahedron. The vector equilibrium shown in the picture is sub-patterned with a two-fold, modular frequency, edge and radius subdivision. Both *radial* and *circumferential* frequencies, of modular subdivision of the *vector equilibrium* are always, everywhere, equal, in both magnitude and number. The *volume* of the *vector* equilibrium is always *twenty times frequency to the third power,* written as $20\,v^3$. The vector equilibrium is also known as an isotropic vector matrix. The vertices of the vector equilibrium of any frequency are always congruent with spheres of equal radius in "closest packing" (see figure 2, in which the fourth row of spheres, in closest packing, show vector equilibrium models of two, three and four frequencies, respectively). The *number of the vertices* in the vector equilibrium, which are always the same as the *number of the spheres* in omni-symmetrical, closest packing, are always: *frequency to the second power times ten plus two*—written as $10\,v^2 + 2$.

Fig. 4a. This structure was made at Washington University, St. Louis, in 1953 under my invention and design instruction. You may possibly be looking at the prototype of the structural principles that we may use in sending history's first (little) *scientific dwelling* to the moon. As you see, all the structural members are tightly bundled together in parallel so that they may be transported in minimum volume within a rocket capsule. The parallel-strut bundles of light-weight magnesium alloy consist of sets of three, fastened together at one end with ball joints clustering them in tripods. Each set is like a camera tripod with three tubular magnesium legs. Each set has ball joints at the tripod *head*. All the tripods' *feet* are also fastened together with ball joints in clusters of five and six tubular-tripod feet per ball joint. We have a little mast coming out of the top of each tripod. This mast is pushed out automatically by a piston in a cylinder mounted in each tripod *head*. We put 200 pounds of gas pressure inside the cylinder and the gas pressure, when triggered by a lanyard, will push the masts of all the tripods outwardly from each of the tripod heads. The pushed-out masts each have three tension members leading to their respective tripod's feet. As the masts are pushed out by the 200 pound pressure the tension members pull the legs of the tripods outwardly from one another. The tripods all open wide with their ball joint feet fastened together in hexagons and pentagons. There is a triangular net of aircraft cable in a regular geodesic "star" spherical grid that restrains the tripod legs from moving any further outwardly from one another than is necessary to form a symmetrical *geodesic dome* or *sphere*, which can be done in 45 seconds.

Fig. 4b. The students pull the lanyard, unleashing the pressured gas to transform the flying seed pod's parallel arrangement strut assembly into a geodesic one-third sphere.

Fig. 4c. Flying seed pod in opened condition: adequate for heavy stressing, yet the 100 pound structure encloses three car space.

4a

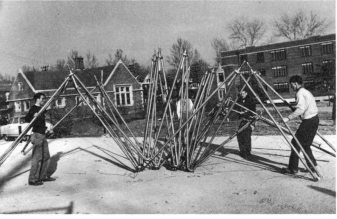

4b

4c

figure the relative acceleration curves in the drag tank pattern tests for a ship like the *Queen Mary*. Then the points along the curves are graphically accommodated by translation through analytical geometry, and geometrical identification of the relative positions of the various points in a three-dimensional grid cube of XYZ coordinates.

By 1913 I saw that man had come to regard the three-dimensional coordinate system as exclusively fundamental. But, I thought that while the XYZ coordination served useful purposes it might also be possible that nature had some other quite superior, rational and comprehensive kind of coordinate system. This occurred to me because the XYZ coordinate system inherently requires recognition of such irrationalities as *pi* and the paradoxial recognition that we cannot finitely subdivide the circumference of a finite circle by its radius. There are a great many irrational numbers occurring as "fundamental" constants in the mathematical coordination between mutually remote scientific disciplines which I thought might be the consequence of our arbitrary use of the XYZ coordinate system. Chemistry seemed to laugh at our coordinate awkwardness as nature contrived all of our physical "matter" entirely out of rational, whole integer simplexes.

If the XYZ, 90 degree coordinate system were not the one employed by nature, then the awkward roughness of the XYZ's irrational constants would be understandable. This was made evident to me while I was in the Navy. Looking back at the wake of my ship one day in 1917, I became interested in its beautiful white path. I said to myself, "That path is white because of the different refractions of light by the bubbles of water—H_2O (not $H_{pi}O$). The bubbles are beautiful little spheres. I wonder how many bubbles I am looking at stretching miles astern?"

I began to make calculations of how many bubbles there were per cubic foot of water. I began to find that in calculating the ship's white wake I was dealing in quintillions to the fourth power times quintillions to the fourth power or some such fantastically absurd number of bubbles. And nature was making those bubbles in sublimely swift ease!

Any time one looks carefully at a bubble, one is impressed with the beauty of its structure, its beautiful sphericity glinting with the colors of the spectrum. It is ephemeral—elegantly conceived, beautifully manufactured and readily broken.

Inasmuch as the kind of mathematics I had learned of in school required the use of the XYZ coordinate system and the necessity of employing *pi* in calculating the spheres, I won-dered "to how many decimal places does nature carry out *pi* before she decides that the computation can't be concluded?" Next I wondered, "to how many arbitrary decimal places does nature carry out the transcendental irrational before she decides to say it's a bad job and call it off?" If nature uses *pi* she has to do what we call *fudging* of her design which means improvising, compromisingly. I thought sympathetically of nature's having to make all those myriad frustrated decisions each time she made a bubble. I didn't see how she managed to formulate the wake of every ship while managing the rest of the universe if she had to make all those decisions. So I said to myself, "I don't think nature uses *pi*. I think she has some other mathematical way of coordinating her undertakings."

It seemed preposterous to go on trying to force nature to explain herself through our awkward XYZ coordinate system. Recital of this 1917 event will have given you a close-up on what I am convinced must be the mental reorientation necessary to comprehension of the principles governing structures.

The most economical spherical agglomerations, i.e., "the closest packing of spheres," we now find to hold the mathematical clues to the principles of coordination governing natural structure—governing the dynamic, vectorial geometry of the atomic nucleus as well as of the atoms themselves. Over and over again we are confronted by nature obviously formulating her structures with beautiful spherical agglomerations (Fig. 2). This began to interest me very much. I found that spheres coordinate, not in 90 degreeness, but in 60 degreeness. Just take three billiard balls and you will find that they *pack* beautifully into a triangle. If you arrange four of them on the billiard table in a square they tend to be restless and to roll around on each other and if compacted to a condition of stability they form a 60 degree angled diamond shape made of two stable triangles.

The physicists find that spheres always form omni-triangulated structures in their closest packing. The frequency phenomena studied in quantum mechanics are all predicated upon agglomerations of spheres of given—i.e., known—radii. All the coordinating is done in spheres of given sizes whose radii are subdivided finitely in modular wave lengths of discrete frequencies. Furthermore, spheres of given sizes are always compacted in omni-triangulation of 60 degreeness, so that six spheres pack most tightly around one sphere on a billiard table and twelve spheres around one in omni-directional compacting. Additional rings of spheres may be tightly compacted around the sphere on the billiard table as symmetrical hexagon patterns and additional layers may be added omni-directionally around one nuclear sphere in symmetrical vector equilibrium growth. The number of spheres in the successively enclosing shells are 12, 42, 92, 162, 252 and so on, which calculates as *ten* times the *frequency* (of radial or circumferential modular subdivisions) to the second power, plus two.

If we accept 60 degreeness we find that instead of getting only four right triangles around a point in a plane, or eight cubes around a point in space, we get six 60 degree angles about the point in the plane, and 20 tetrahedra around one point in space. Furthermore the circumferential modular frequency of planar or omni-directional patterning will always be in one-to-one correspondence with the radial frequencies of modular subdividing. When we do this, we find we have made a model of the spontaneously coordinate structure which nature actually uses (Fig. 3).

In demonstrating this to yourself, remember that the eight cubes around one point in space represent the three dimensions of 90 degreeness. However, when dealing with the 60 degree coordination of tetrahedra, which are the volumes bound by the planes of four edge-joined triangles, you will find that you can get fourth power or "four-dimensional" accommodation of space around a point as computed in the terms of linear module frequency of either radius or circumference of the pattern system (which also is to say that linear and angular accelerations are in one-to-one correspondence). You can get twenty tetrahedra around one point, $2^4 + 2^2 = 20$. Anyone using the tetrahedral concept in coordinating geometry and arithmetic would find that four-dimensionality is not an inconceivable or nonconceptual mystery but a very simple, modelable and rational relationship arrived at by closest packing together of equi-volume tetrahedra around one point.

Late in the nineteenth century the organic chemists led by van't Hoff, discovered that all organic chemistry is tetrahedrally configured. In all the structuring we know of in organic chemistry—plastics or gasolines or what-have-you —the atoms form molecules by little tetrahedral arrangements: tetrahedra point-to-point (univalent), tetrahedra edge-to-edge (bivalent), tetrahedra face-to-face (trivalent), or congruent tetrahedra (quadrivalent). These are the primary bondings. The range goes from C (carbon), which is relatively light, to C_4 (carbonaceous diamond), which is quadrivalent: four points of the tetrahedra are congruent with one another.

After X-ray diffraction in 1932, Linus Pauling, who received the Nobel Prize for his pioneering exploration of

Fig. 4d. The principle of structural dynamics of the Washington University, St. Louis, moon structure, the flying seed pod, and its logistic pattern transformability, are doubly interesting because they have turned out to be also the same structural, self-realization system employed by a class of microcosmic structures—the protein shells of all the different types of viruses. About three and one half years ago molecular biologists in England and their colleagues in America, working in teams, were trying to discover the structural characteristics of the protein shells of the viruses with X-ray diffraction photographic analysis. These virus scientists discovered that the viruses' protein shells were all some type of spherical geodesic structure. Having previously seen published pictures of my geodesic structures they corresponded with me and I was able to give them the mathematics and show them how and why these structures occur and behave as they do. They have now found the polio virus structure, pictured here, to be the same structure as the "possible moon structure". The polio virus, instead of having the tripods on the outside and the clusters of five and six feet on the inside, has the five- and six-way jointings outside and the tripods or three-ways on the inside. The pictured model of the protein shell of the polio virus was made by Dr. Donald L. D. Caspar, nuclear physicist, Director of the Children's Cancer Research of the Boston Children's Hospital, Boston, a colleague of the English virological team at Cavendish Laboratory. The number of "humps" or structural clusters of five or six prismatic sectioned struts of the protein shells of the virus follows my law of $10\,v^2 + 2$.

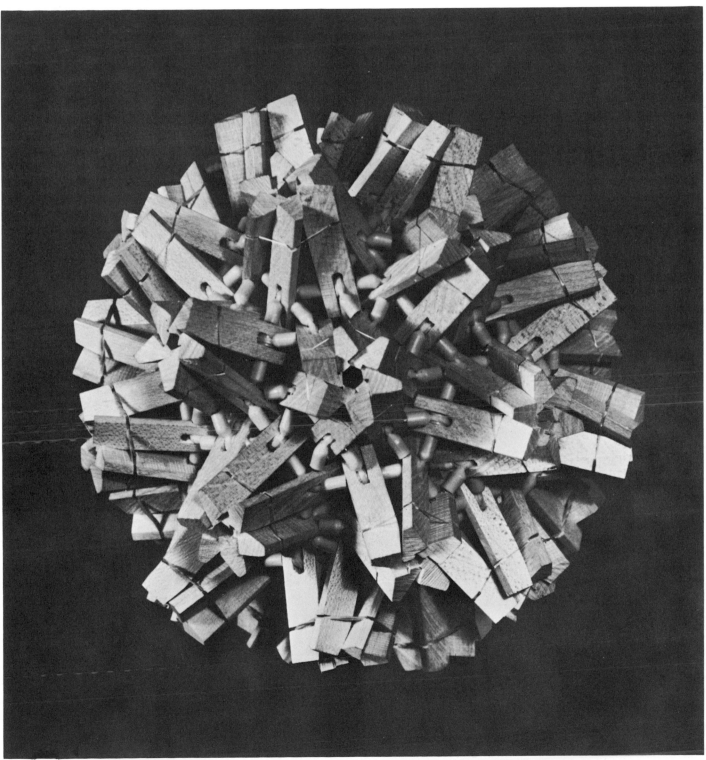

4d

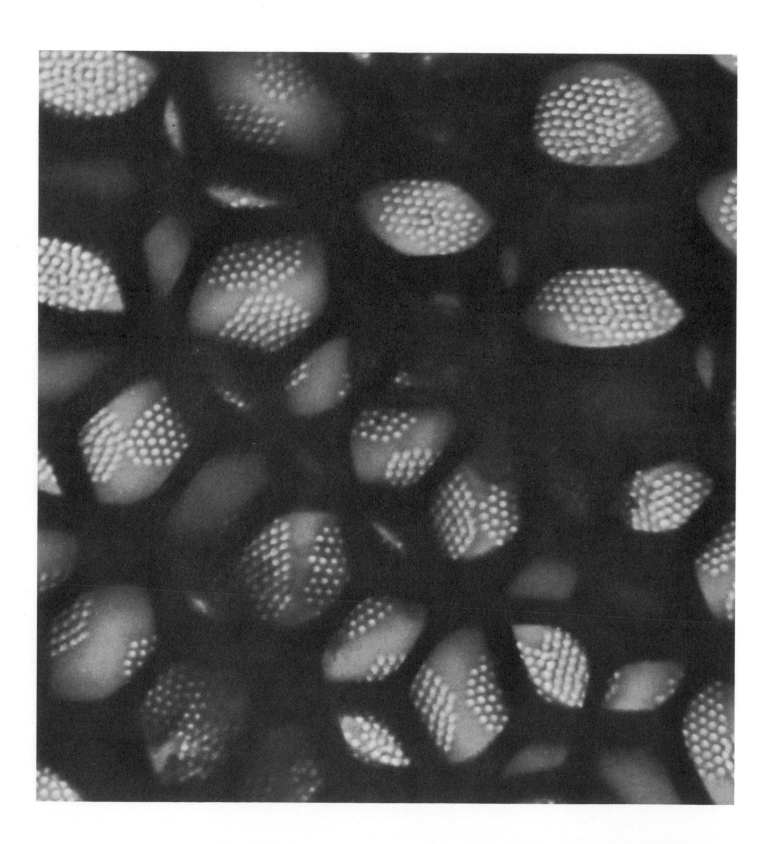

Fig. 5a. Micro-morphologist Dr. Helmcke of the Max Planck Institute, Berlin, and also of the Berlin Technical University, using the electron microscope, in 1962 photographed the algae known as diatoms—silicon dioxide, water-borne microplants which also proved to be structural derivatives of our same vector equilibrium coordinated, geodesic, spherical structures.

Fig. 5b. Model of one of my geodesic "Fly's Eye", basketry-tensegrity, three-quarter sphere, twelve-frequency structures. This model was made preparatory to development of the Yomiuri, 150 ft. dome, opened in Japan in April, 1964.

chemical structuring, began to discover that metals were also tetrahedrally coordinated and inter-linked, not point-to-point but through one another as chains are linked, with dynamically coordinate or coincident gravitational centers. If we think of six-edged chain-links (remembering that the tetrahedron is a six-edged pyramidal frame) we can envision the manner in which we may link tetrahedra in six different directions. That multi-directional connectability explains the way in which metals are linked together. Now combining van't Hoff and Pauling and our own experimental explorations, we may dare to guess that because experimental chemistry has as yet found no contradiction to tetrahedronal linkage, despite vast probing, that *all the structuring of nature is probably done by rational tetrahedronal increment coordination* in which the XYZ coordinates also may be employed to describe the arrangements but only in awkward irrationality because of the cube edges' inherent irrationality in respect to their cubic face diagonals' hypotenuse values, which hypotenuses are the edges of the tetrahedra in the omni-directional matrix of vectors of the natural structuring itself. The contemporary development of giant electronic computers makes the handling of the XYZ awkwardness a practical matter but serves to obscure the significance of my discovery of nature's own rational, non-simultaneous vectorial coordinate system oriented to the tetrahedron-octahedron lattice and its importance to fundamental clarity of thinking in a democratically-coagulating world bewildered by a "foreign-hieroglyphicking" science.

In February, 1962, the *New York Herald Tribune* newspaper reported that at a world conference of molecular biologists, Dr. Horne of Cambridge University, England, had announced the discovery of the generalized principles governing the structuring of the protein shells of all the viruses. All these virus structures had proved to be geodesic spheres of various frequencies. The scientists reported that not only were the viruses geodesic structures, which latter had been discovered earlier by Buckminster Fuller, but also that the mathematics which apparently controls nature's formulations of the viruses also had been discovered (1933) and published by Fuller a number of years earlier (1944). This mathematics was the Energetic/Synergetic Geometry, i.e., the mathematical coordinate system of nature's closest packing which I have already mentioned a few paragraphs earlier which is omni-tetrahedronally coordinate. See Figures 4a-4d.

The virus structures are at present in the critical focus of science's spotlight for within the protein shells the nucleic acid contains the 4 digit coded controls of all the variations in nature's biological structuring design. Furthermore, the virus and its nucleic acid occur on that extraordinary threshold in which the physical phenomena could be identified either as animate or inanimate. Moreover, it is in this particular virus, protein, nucleic acid area that the first tentative clues to the comprehension of cancer are most hopefully searched for by science. Because this area probably contains both the keys to life's structuring and destructuring, the ranks of the molecular biologists have been powerfully augmented by physicists, chemists, mathematicians and the exquisitely probing tools of those sciences.

Though the relative amount of science budgeted money

5c

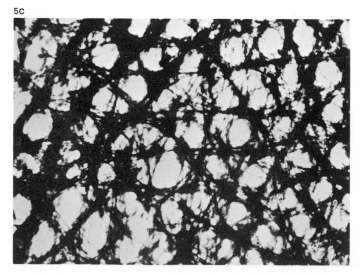

5d

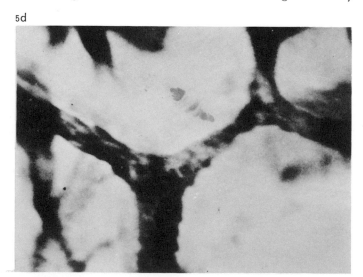

76

going to this kind of life probing and protecting research is but a minor fraction of the wealth reinvestments going toward scientific development in rocketry, atomics and weapons in general, we can say that of the portion of science allocated money going toward medical and biological investigation a large share of the medical funds goes in the direction of the virus and nucleic acid inquiry.

That the mathematics which I had long ago discovered as seemingly employed by nature in her comprehensive coordinate system has now been validated by these molecular biologist teams means that much of the invisible structuring of nature which was heretofore thought of as being nonconceptual as well is now proving to be conceptually comprehendible.

Early in 1962, Dr. Helmcke, a micro-morphologist of the Max Planck Institute in Berlin, discovered with the electron microscope that the structures of the algae, which are chemically comprised of silicon dioxide and are also spoken of as diatoms, accomplish much of their structuring in the most sophisticated geodesic manner which also employs the same Energetic/Synergetic mathematical coordinating system that I had discovered as operative in many other formulations of nature (Figs. 5a–5h).

Ten years ago we discovered that the radiolaria, which are of the ocean dwelling amoeba family (Fig. 6), also employ both the geodesic structuring and the Energetic/Synergetic Geometry in their self-formulation. The diatoms are plants and the radiolaria are animals so we find that whereas the geodesic structuring principles and the Energetic/Synergetic Geometry principles were first discovered by science as

Fig. 5c. Dr. Arthur H. C. von Hochstetter, Head of the Department of Anatomy, Faculty of Medicine, University of Western Ontario, London, Prov. of Ontario, has succeeded in silver-staining the *albuginea testis* of the adult human. Pictured is a small fragment of the most superficial layer of *pers serosa* of albuginea which, as Dr. von Hochstetter says, "discloses the geodesic dome structure—patterns with hexagons, pentagons and triangles forming six-pointed stars. The unit stars are about 40 mu in diameter. This area of the subepithelial layer probably was bulged outwards due to tissue or lymph fluid. Therefore, the geodesic dome structure."

Fig. 5d. Dr. von Hochstetter also succeeded in micro-photographing the structure of the cornea of the human eyeball. Dr. von Hochstetter says, "The cornea, the most regular shaped structure of the body, consists of interwoven bands of unyielding collagenic fibres that are arranged in many lamellae. This fibrous architecture includes a dense meshwork of cells. In these specimens the injection of a mixture of India-ink and Gelatin into the Cornea has partly filled the space-system in which the cells lie. The figures formed by the cast indicate that the cells are arranged in a three-dimensional geodesic grid of the tetrahedronal type. The various hexagonal or polygonal figures (holes of the grid) are from 10 to 100 micron in diameter."

Fig. 5e. Dr. von Hochstetter also succeeded, by the same gelatin and ink staining method, in micro-photographing the structure of the cornea of the eye of a cow which clearly discloses the three-way multi-frequency geodesic grid.

5e

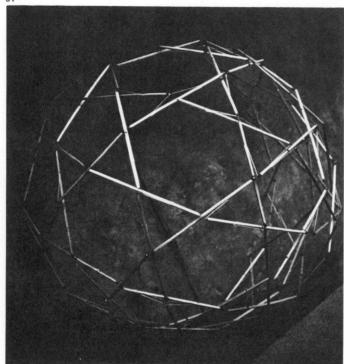

Fig. 5f. Model of Fuller's six-frequency geodesic, three-way, *tensegrity*, three-quarter sphere, showing the hexagon, pentagon, star patterning, similar to that of Dr. von Hochstetter's anatomical spheriodal structures.

Fig. 5g. Twelve-frequency, tensegrity, geodesic, three-quarter sphere dome, in which the spaces between compression components have been reduced to "kissing contact" because of reduction of distance between mid-arch and mid-chord of spherical dimensions, occurring as frequency is increased, ergo, central angles of spheres are decreased. Note the same star truss patterning as in Dr. von Hochstetter's cornea structures.

Fig. 5h. 384 ft. diameter geodesic dome of Union Tank Car Company, Wood River, Illinois, installed in 1960. "Clear-span" means "without interior, space-interrupting supports." This 384 ft. "clear-span" geodesic structure can enclose an entire American size football field, together with its end zones and circumferential running track, as well as generous side-line bleachers. The size of this dome may be appreciated by the scale of stature of three men working on a ventilator near the top (right) of the dome. This geodesic dome is large enough to completely cover the world's second largest cathedral, in Seville, Spain. The weight of the 384 ft. Wood River steel frame and skin geodesic is the same as the combined weight of only three of the forest of stone columns providing the interior support of Seville Cathedral, whose enormous weight also includes the exterior stone structure and its flying buttresses. There are now thousands of geodesic structures erected in fifty countries around the earth, to which they have usually been delivered by air. Employing the fundamental principles of nature's structuring, the average of all the geodesic domes to date enclose space at approximately one percent of the weight of materials required by conventional architectural and engineering structures of equivalent volume designed for equivalent load-stresses and clear-span environment controls.

employed only in explaining self-structuring behaviors of viruses on the threshold between animate and inanimate phenomenon, that the same structural and mathematical principles are later also found to be operating at the much larger and more complex level of "life," also in the single cell plants and animals, the diatoms and the radiolaria.

We next discovered that all life cell structures (no matter how complex the total association may be) and all bubble complexes are characterized by 14 faceted, webbed, chambers, the 14 facets being of an infinite variety of asymmetrical polygon sizings but always of 14 facets. These 14 facets are then to be identified with the tetrahedron's *4 faces plus 6 edges plus 4 vertexes* which prime aspects total 14. Tetrahedrons of very high frequency composition which result from piling up a triangular pyramid of ping-pong balls (or of any spheres of the same size) can be truncated on each of their edges or each of their four vertexes by knocking off balls which adds 6 facets and 4 facets respectively to the four original faces. By simply increasing the frequency of the basic layers of the spheres, the truncation of the edges or vertexes may be so patterned with the faces in such a manner as to result in "any" polygonal shapes of a total of 14 facets (Figs. 7a—7e).

It is appropriate at this point to quote Robert W. Marks,

in his book, *The Dymaxion World of Buckminster Fuller* (Reinhold Publishing Company, 1960). "An interesting confirmation of some of Fuller's assumptions of the relation of Energetic Geometry to atomic structures was given, in 1958, by John J. Grebe, Director of Nuclear and Basic Research, Dow Chemical Company, in a paper, 'A Periodic Table for Fundamental Particles,' delivered before the New York Academy of Sciences.

"The mass of the various grouped subatomic particles, Grebe stated, 'is highly reminiscent of a relation pointed out some years ago by R. B. Fuller in a report explaining the problem of building into a structure the maximum strength and rigidity with the minimum material. Fuller's solution involves the equivalent of tripods or balloons placed in closely packed cubic pattern. . . . These models could represent the structure of the so-called elemental particles mathematically, although not necessarily physically—too little is known to say that. However, it does seem as if these successive layers are significant in the properties—particularly the slow neutron cross sections—of isotopes, from the smallest nuclear masses to those of the twenty-sixth shell, and including both lead and bismuth.' "

We may now combine physicist John Grebe's identification of the atomic nucleus self-structural patterning with Buckminster Fuller's tetrahedronally coordinate Energetic/Synergetic Geometry and combine the Grebe discovery with Linus Pauling's discovery of tetrahedronally coordinate inorganic chemistry with the latest information on tetrahedronally coordinate structuring at the virus level and the radiolaria and diatom levels and also with the inanimate bubble and the animate cell truncated tetrahedronal coordination and realize that an entirely new era of fundamental conceptuality has been discovered in all the morphological contriving of nature.

Sir Charles Snow has gone into literary world orbit blasted off by the powerful way in which he has presented the abyss existing between the worlds of science and the humanities. Snow traces the now seemingly unspannable void between the two worlds back to the early antipathy of literary men toward science and technology at the beginnings of industrialization on the one hand and on the other to the conscious or sub-conscious obscurationism of the early scientists who were heedless of the literary man's scientific illiteracy and the latter's consequent intuitive insecurity which in turn bred his antipathy. The literary men were the only potential liaison men between science and the public ken, ergo, the public gradually knew less and less of the scientific evolution that was pacing industrialization. Today humanity is bewildered by the utter power for good or evil vested in a scientific activity of which they and their literary interpreters know little or naught.

I personally surmise however that the real break between science and the public occurred when science found that invisible behaviors of nature could be ferreted out by instruments and computationally mastered without recourse to conceptual models, which had become seemingly invalid due to the inability to model fourth dimensionality with X, Y, Z 90° coordination, which however could be readily computed mathematically. With the wholesale migration of science into the world of invisibility without any conceptual models of reference, the literary man who depended upon conceptual models or analogies for his verbal pattern relaying was automatically excluded from either ring-side participation or back row glimpsing of the significant affairs of science.

The natural four axis, 60 degree, tetrahedronal coordinate system which I have described to you now returns "conceptuality" of dynamic structural principles to scientific validity.

The brush and chisel artists who, despite the literary

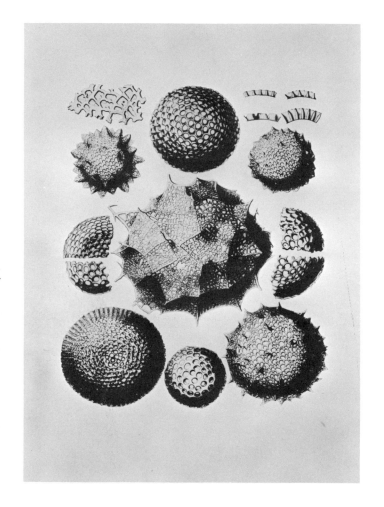

Fig. 6. Subvisible microscopic animal structures called *radiolaria* are developed by the same mathematical and structural laws as those governing the man-designed geodesic and other non-man-designed spheriodal structures of nature.

man's frustrations, tried to *follow* the scientists into "non-conceptuality" with their "non-representational" quasi-abstractions are now proven to have been intuitively sound in their conviction that they could really follow or even lead science in the game of intuitive probing. In a sense science behaved more ignorantly than the artists, but the artists' pursuit of science with its various phases of abstraction forsook the *conceptually reasonable* requirements of the literary man who has been held by society to be the public's interpreter of the significance of the total inventory of evoluting realities. James Joyce to a mild extent and Gertrude Stein to a considerable extent attempted to go along with the brush and chisel abstractionists in following the scientists into non-conceptual validity of reasoning, but by and large the world public was left incommunicado by both science and modern art. Both the scientists and the artists themselves became defensively bewildered by the overall and unexpected emergences of major crises of man with none of which emergencies either blind- flying science or blind-man's-buffing art could cope, either positively or negatively.

With the return to valid, rationally computable conceptuality of nature's dynamic formulating, there returns to literary man the ability to re-establish the communication integrity of science and world society. The rate of re-establishment of conceptual comprehension of scientific frontiering and its technical, ergo economic, ergo practical significance, will be painfully slow to those who now have discovered nature's sublimely rational comprehensibility. It may take a whole new generation but that is an historically short period for so vital a recovery from world society's present intellectual comprehension tail-spinning.

What is the most probable way in which the effective reorientation of man will occur in switching from non-conceptual floundering to valid conceptual coordination? It may quite logically occur in major degree as a spontaneous by-product of the way in which man now evolves his environment-controlling structural advantages in a myriad of new techno-scientific enterprises such as colonization on the moon, in which both environment controlling and local metabolic process controlling present far more demanding tasks than man has ever before been faced with, all of which require economy of physical resource investment at a level of energy utilization effectiveness never before operative in the affairs of man.

The validity of my conjecture is to be apprehended in the omni-science concentrated attention to the building of a fifteen story high rocket in contrast to the utter lack of

7a

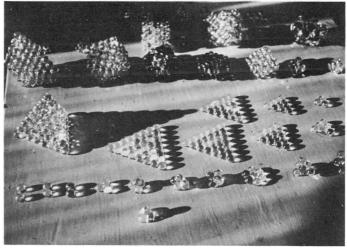

7b

Fig. 7a. Isotropic vector-matrix demonstrates ability of asymmetrically terminalled high-frequency energy vectors to accommodate any structural shape.

Fig. 7b. Closest packed spheres of the isotropic vector-matrix provide both the asymmetrical and symmetrical shapes.

scientist involvement in the design of our presently most common fifteen story apartment houses and the contrast in the rocket's and apartment house's relative structural and mechanical performances per pounds of invested materials.

Consider the nonsense of attempting to put a new city apartment house into orbit. What would happen if our conceptual principles of fundamental structuring were broadly applied to man's everyday structural problems may be ascertained as follows. Experiment shows that cubes are invalid as structural devices, although the building industry and society in general commonly think of buildings in terms of cubes or quadrangular coordination. If you make a little cube of twelve toothpicks, and join their ends with soft rubber balls you will find that the cube wobbles and collapses whereas a tetrahedron made in the same way, with six toothpicks and soft rubber ball vertexial jointing is utterly stable. The cube becomes rhombic. Each little square will flatten down very readily. The tetrahedron is made up entirely of triangles which are the only inherently stable polygons.

Since cubes make such poor structures, the only way that men are able to stabilize the cubical buildings they do build is by going to the corners where the members come together at 90 degrees and putting in little triangular gusset-plate reinforcings. Sometimes this vertexial triangulation of quadrangular buildings is done with a whole lot of nails, but in a big steel building, it is done by putting in triangular patterns by riveting or welding in the gusseting.

The triangular steel gussets at the corners of interstices of the steel structure must withstand the prying action of the lever arm of the full length of the beam to which each gusset is attached. The builders are able to make the building "stand" because of the excessive use of steel and massive inertia but not because the building is really well designed. Tetrahedrons are inherently "comfortable," do not tend to transform into other shapes while cubes want to collapse. Quadrangularly designing architects and builders are working ignorantly *against* natural forces. If they build in tetrahedronal complexes they are employing natural forces and their buildings are completely stable.

If we draw a line diagonally from corner to corner on each of the six faces of a cube, we find that these six lines turn out to be the outlines of a tetrahedron. These hidden tetrahedra in "solid" cubes make the cube stand up. Let us now reconsider the triangular gusset plates in the corners of the cubical buildings of steel, fighting the long lever beams attached to them. Quite clearly, if we made the triangular

7c

Fig. 7c. Closest packed spheres provide tetrahedra or truncated tetrahedra. Because $4 + 4 + 6 = 14$, truncating the *four* vertices, plus *four* faces, plus *six* edges of the tetrahedron provides the fourteen faces of the vector equilibrium. High-frequency agglomerations, asymmetrically truncated, account for all the shapes of all living tissue cell structures, as well as for all the shapes of bubble agglomerations, all of which are fourteen-faceted chambers.

Fig. 7d. Bubble agglomerations disclosing fourteen-faceted, asymmetrical chambering.

82

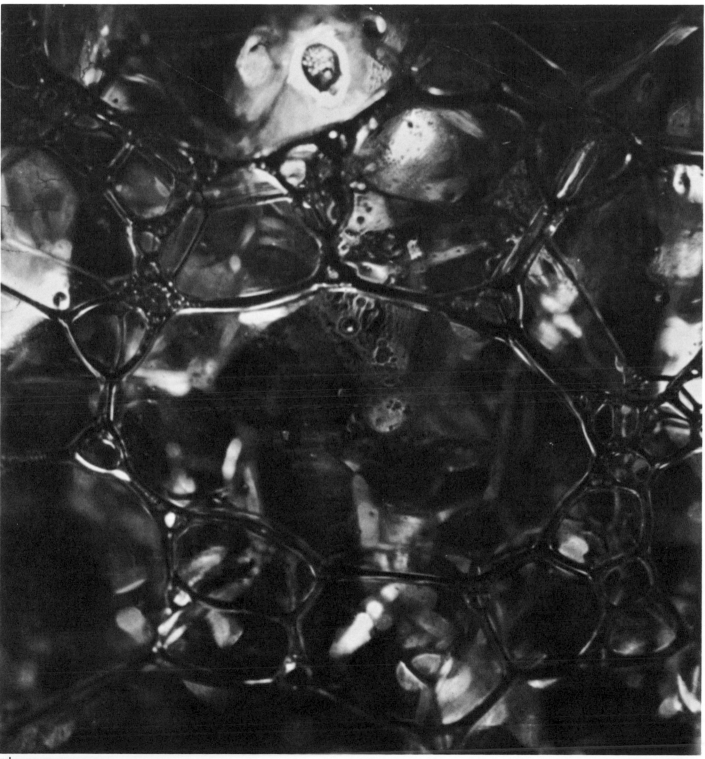

7d

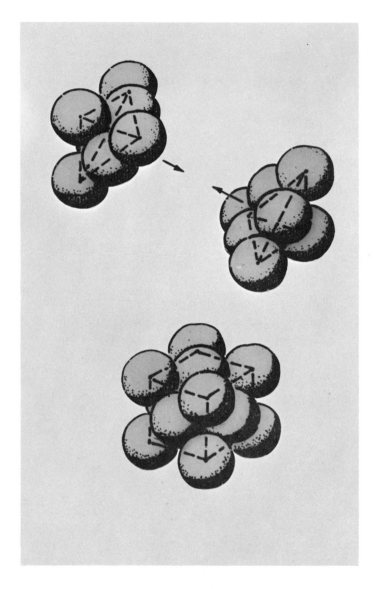

Fig. 7e. Two pairs of seven-ball, triangular sets of closest packed spheres precess to associate as the cube. Precess means for two or more bodies to move in an interrelationship pattern of other than 180 degrees, in this case in a 60 degree "twist", in respect to one another. This cube consists of fourteen spheres, whose number corresponds to the fourteen tetrahedronal facets, the fourteen faces of the vector equilibrium, and the fourteen faces of Lord Kelvin's tetraxideca, the all-space filling, fourteen-faceted symmetrical polyhedron of eight hexagons and six squares. The cube shown is the minimum cube which may be stably produced by closest packed spheres. Eight spheres will not close pack as a cube and are utterly unstable.

gusset plates a little larger they would be more effective in opposing the beams' leverage against them. If we increase the size of the gusset triangles progressively they ultimately become the diagonals of the quadrangular openings of the buildings and correspond to the six edges of the tetrahedrons hidden in the cubical or quadrangular building scheme.

As our heritage of the milleniums of man's limited knowledge of his "world" in which it was seemingly obvious that the world was flat, squares and parallel lines proved adequate for local mensuration but the square grids of our townships were found by surveyors to be inherently non-associable either as a continental or a world grid. As a consequence, world resurveying began a half century ago on a workable triangular grid. This structural reasoning parallels the findings of chemistry, wherein nature's structures are all tetrahedronally coordinate in both organic and inorganic compounds. We begin to appreciate the paradox of man trying to force his behavioral explanations of a tetrahedral nature into a cubical framework. It was the cubical framework arbitrarily adopted by man as his "frame of reference" which was awkward. Nature was not at all awkward. When we accept a tetrahedral coordinating in arithmetical computing of structure the utterly rational relationships found in chemistry reveal themselves. All we need to do is to both say and think of "triangling" increments instead of "squaring" increments when we use the arithmetical notation of X^2; and say and think "tetrahedroning" increments instead of "cubing" increments when we use the arithmetical notation X^3; and when we write or discover X^4 we find that it is comfortably modelable in kindergarten structural techniques (Figs. 8a—8d).

Now let me discuss ways in which we might think about nature's *logistical* strategy in accomplishment of most economic world-around structuring as disclosed to us within the narrow dimensional limits of immediately visible nature. Let us use the tree as an example. Trees are substantial organic structures, and they frequently last for many years more than do men or birds or fish or the contrived dwellings or nests of men or other mobile life. Some trees stand for more than a thousand years against great storms and earthquakes. While man and birds and fish are positionally mobile, trees are not. Trees are only locally flexible. And yet trees spread their population around the world. The way they do this is by means of their seeds which they place in beautiful little flying machines. The maple tree's seeds, for example, float around in the winds and come fluttering down like little helicopters. The winds carry these seeds so that by successive generations trees are able to go airborne into new locations around the world. Thus are accomplished the world's pine tree belt and palm tree belt, and other world-girdling tree belts.

Let us consider the logistics nature uses in building and distributing such a lasting structure as a tree. We find that in the seed nature provides a blueprint pattern tightly folded up in a triangular tension grid. There are two ways of differentiating structure: into tensional behaviors and into compressional behaviors. Compression behaviors are disassociative while tensional behaviors are inherently associative and spontaneously cohering. These two structural behaviors—tension and compression—are never innocent of one another, never independent. Nevertheless, we think of a column as a compression member and a rope or cable as a tension member. But the rope, when tensed axially, contracts or goes into compression transversely in its girth. The compression column's girth goes into tension. Predominately *tension* members have an *unlimited* ratio of length to diameter of cross section, whereas predominately *compression* members are inherently *limited* in this respect. The Greeks learned that the height of a stone column could not exceed eighteen times its diameter. A steel column can be a little higher—about thirty to one. But in tension there is no such limit of length to section, and we can make great ropes of steel, and from them bridges over a mile long, with only a two- or three-foot-thick cable. The stronger the alloy of the steel, the slenderer we can make the cable in respect to its length.

There is no limit ratio, structurally speaking, no limit to the tensional coherence of the atoms and the patterns that they provide for man (man does not invent these phenomena). Enormous tasks can be done in tension. For instance, a whole locomotive can be lifted up and into a ship with a very delicate tension cable compared to the size of the column which would be needed to push it up an equal distance. In tension there is much higher lifting performance per pound.

So nature, in arranging for one tree to build another tree, makes up a folded, tight blueprint in a tension network grid and folds it into a tight package: a seed. When the seed comes to rest, nature then provides the means for expanding the tree pattern by means of locally available compression components developed from the local water and air. Water is highly non-compressible—our powerful hydraulic pumps exploit this—so when nature builds a tree, she takes the blueprint of the seed and begins to pump it up,

Fig. 8a. The numbers of squares and the numbers of triangles enclosed, respectively, by two, three, and four frequency of equimodule edge subdivisions of large, gridded squares and triangles are four, nine, and sixteen. We may say "triangling" instead of "squaring". When we say "triangling" we are referring to stable structures. When we say "squaring" we are referring to unstable shapes. Because squares are utterly unstable they may not be called structures. Squares, when partially stabilized, always consist of two triangles which can move in respect to one another as the two halves of a hinge. When we deal with *triangling* we are being more economical with space than when we employ squares with edges equal to the triangles'. Nature always insists on being most economical. Nature "triangles". Nature accounts all of her structuring entirely *rationally* when measuring with triangles. At the bottom of the picture we see, at left, *any* asymmetrical quadrangle. At the bottom, right, *any* asymmetrical triangle. Bisecting the edges of each and interconnecting we discover that the subdivision quadrangles are inherently dissimilar. That is, their respective angles and edges do not correspond and are all of different magnitudes, whereas the subdivisions of triangles correspond, inherently, as "similar" and "identical." Ergo: *triangular observation* of physical phenomena from any angle always produces reliable and rational accounting not available in quadrangular accounting.

full of locally available water. She then develops regenerative patterns, using the inhibition of more and more local waters. More water is needed because so much keeps leaking out, through the process known as osmosis.

It is the non-compressibility of the water which makes for that great sturdy stiffness of a tree also permitting a tree trunk to hold out a branch weighing from ten to twenty-five tons to be waved flexibly in the wind. How can it wave in the wind? Because in between the molecules of non-compressible water, nature pushes in little packages of air, little spheroids. Air is highly compressible (as in pneumatic tires), so the little molecules of air compress like an automobile tire, allowing the branch to wave.

Nature's great trick in making trees is to distribute tensional blueprints which regenerate the pattern locally, employing the compressions of local gases and local waters, enclosing them in beautiful tensional skins of the molecules themselves. This is nature's major strategy of efficient energy utilization in the distribution of structures.

I myself began to initiate such a "regenerative tree" strategy in experimental undertakings in structures about a third of a century ago. I gave myself the task of exploring the practicality of assembling the components of buildings under the most preferred conditions of technology and science, in order to achieve a very high degree of efficiency. This collection of components had to be capable of economical air transport to any part of the earth. I saw that the essentials were local hydraulics and pneumatics and generalized tensional packages—broadly speaking. Familiar examples of this are all kinds of pneumatic structures, from inflatable toy seahorses and life rafts to dirigibles. Beyond these, there are very complex structures. For examples, I have made geodesic domes—omni-triangulated spheres— with pneumatic components. Geodesic tensegrity spheres are highly magnified, pneumatic principle structures.

The hydraulics possibilities include the local cements, water, air, gravel, sand and rocks. The economic theory behind prestressed concrete is based on pre-fabrication and shipping only the small bulk of steel as a tensional sinew system, and applying the local water, sand, gravel, and cement as the building bulk. The particles which make up cement are sifted sand and gravel, which, though they look rough, pack averagedly as spheres would pack—in 60-degree angular packing. Few people think of cement that way, but if it is shaken down, agitated well, and lubricated together with a colloid, it will automatically avail itself of nature's tetrahedral structuring in "closest packing" pattern.

8b

8c

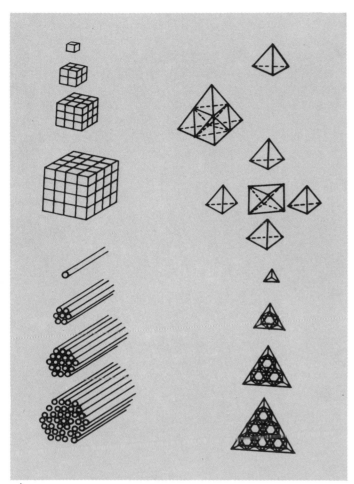

8d

Fig. 8b, 8c. Shows "cubing" vs. "tetrahedroning". In each case we have "two-frequency" edge-module subdivisioning. The (big) two-frequency cube subdivides into eight little cubes. The (big) two-frequency tetrahedron subdivides into four little tetrahedra—each one-eighth the volume of the big tetrahedron—plus one octahedron whose volume must be equal to *four* little tetrahedra, because we know that when we double the linear dimension of a solid figure we always increase its volume eightfold; *and* the edges of the four little tetrahedra, as well as all the edges of the octahedron, are each one-half of the edge length of the (big) two-frequency tetrahedron; four little tetra plus one octa (of same edge length) equal eight little tetrahedra, of our big two-frequency octahedron.

Fig. 8d. This picture shows that we may say "tetrahedroning" instead of "cubing". Corresponding large tetrahedra and cubes, consisting of *two, three* and *four* frequency equimodular subdivision of their edges, respectively demonstrate *volumes* of *eight, twenty-seven,* and *sixty-four tetrahedra or cubes,* as measured in terms of the small tetrahedronal or cubic components of each big tetrahedron or cube. The volume of a cube whose facial diagonals are the same length as those of a regular tetrahedron will be exactly three times the volume of that size tetrahedron. When we account *all space* with tetrahedra we are three times as economical as when we account it with cubes. Nature always uses the most economical. Twenty tetrahedra may surround one point whereas only eight cubes can surround one point. Tetrahedronal accounting of omni-directional space permits rationally componented fourth and fifth power models whereas cubes permit only third power models. Tetrahedra permit realistic, "kindergarten-obvious", "four-dimensional modeling" and more. Of the twenty tetrahedra of equal volume that surround one point, eight are regular and twelve are irregular but each have the same volume as the volume of the regular tetrahedrons involved. The total volume of these eight regular and twelve irregular tetrahedra, symmetrically filling all space around one point, in the shape of the vector-equilibrium, is twenty times one of the regular tetrahedra involved. Twenty identical "isosceles" tetrahedra may symmetrically surround one point in the shape of the regular icosahedron, with a total volume of 18.51, as measured in terms of the regular tetrahedron with a volume of one, in respect to which the vector equilibrium has a volume of twenty. The equilateral vector equilibrium and icosahedron of identical length edges have volumes of twenty and 18.51 respectively. Since I was its discoverer, progressively between 1917–1940, I have given the name Synergetics to the arithmetical-geometrical, chemical, energy-quanta, omni-rational, sixty-degree coordination of nature. In that system the well-known geometrical figures have the following volumetric values, in respect to the tetrahedron as unity, having a volume of one: the octahedron, four; the vector equilibrium, twenty; the cube, three; the rhombic dodecahedron, six; and the tetraxideca, ninety-six—of which the last three constitute all the cases of complete space filling when associated only with themselves.

This principle of tensional blueprints—prestressed concrete is an example—is manifesting itself as the direction which building will take. In order to make the resources of the earth adequate to the needs of all people, we must increase the performance per pound of those resources in a very big way, thus giving man environmental controls. This must be done to accommodate all the new shifting patterns of man around the face of the earth. We will have to employ nature's much more economical, grand logistical strategies. Emulating nature, man must distribute mathematical information as basic pattern, which does not weigh anything at all. The highly technical components of very fine high-tension steels, and aluminums, and fine alloys can then be centrally processed and distributed. Those will be used primarily for tensional functions, and will be rigidified by the local compressional pneumatics and hydraulics. I think this is the most comprehensive statement that I could make regarding the most recent discovery of nature's forever permitted structural strategies. These latter are the most effective and fundamentally economical structural strategies to be employed by man if he is going to be successful in rendering nature's resources adequate to a higher standard of living and enjoyment by 100 per cent of humanity, than any previously privileged historical minority has ever experienced. That is what men are about to do. Those who are versed in fundamental structuring principles will be the next half century's *most needed* men.

STRUCTURE
CONSTRUCTION, TECTONICS

Sometimes we may be close to despair when trying to cope with the visual world through words: the harder we try the more we seem to get lost between shifting and elusive drifts of irrelevancy, inappropriateness or vacuity. Indeed an artist may feel that there is no place at all for verbal formulations in architecture and the visual arts; yet he will not be able to create without guidance from certain principles which he once acquired or formulated and which are in themselves not visual but conceptual. They may be as simple as a determination not to be influenced by any intellectual considerations during the process of creation, or they may be quite numerous and varied, and their validity may extend beyond the individual to an entire group where they appear linked to more general habits of thought and procedure.

How action, thought and language interact has long been a field of philosophical inquiry, and we have been taught to recognize language as a mirror that has to be kept as clear as possible if it is to reflect truly the facts and states of experience. The following brief essay is an attempt to increase clarity in a very limited area by considering three closely related yet distinct concepts which are of particular relevance to discussions of architecture: structure, construction and tectonics.

In colloquial usage the distinction between structure and construction is blurred and the word tectonics is rare. We may refer to a building at times as a structure and at times as a construction without really intending to denote in one case something different from the other. But such looseness seems inadmissible in critical usage, once we begin to think about the very real distinction that exists between the concepts linked to the words, and about the considerable increase in usefulness that accrues to the words if we insist on using them with precision.

In order to accentuate the difference between "structure" and "construction" all that is needed is a simple experiment of substitution: if we substitute "construction of society" or "construction of thought" in a statement where previously we had "structure of society" or "structure of thought" we recognize a drastic difference. While we find ourselves inclined to think of "construction" as the result of an activity which is "to construct," we don't seem to think as easily of "structure" as the result of a conscious activity which is "to structure." The real difference between these two words is that "construction" carries a connotation of something put together consciously while "structure" refers to an ordered arrangement of constituent parts in a much wider sense.

With regard to architecture the exact relationship between structure and construction now appears clear. Structure as the more general and abstract concept refers to a system or principle of arrangement destined to cope with forces at work in a building, such as post-and-lintel, arch, vault, dome and folded plate. Construction on the other hand refers to the concrete realization of a principle or system—a realization which may be carried out in a number of materials and ways. For example, the structural system which we call post-and-lintel may occur in wood, stone and metal and its elements may be fastened together by a number of methods.

The visible and tangible form which results from the process of construction can be discussed and judged in various ways. As far as construction is concerned there are all the questions of selecting and handling materials, of process and technique. As far as structure is concerned it is possible to assess the appropriateness and efficiency of the system that was chosen.

To achieve a desired end in building we may rely on the accumulated strength and mass of assembled materials. This will be a constructional effort. But with a structural change, i.e. a change of arrangement which distributes its materials in another manner, the same end may be achieved in a more elegant fashion. A form may emerge that is a more direct result of, or reply to, the forces at work. In actual practice structural change and constructional effort are, or at least should be, inseparable and in continuous interaction. However, a fine structural system may sometimes find realization in a rather poor construction while something well constructed may be very inefficient from the structural point of view.

When a structural concept has found its implementation through construction, the visual result will affect us through certain expressive qualities which clearly have something to do with the play of forces and corresponding arrangement of parts in the building, yet cannot be described in terms of construction and structure alone. For these qualities, which are expressive of a relation of form to force, the term tectonic should be reserved.

The word *tec*tonics derives from the same Greek root which we find in archi*tec*ture and *tec*hnology: we are reminded of the basic human activity of giving visible shape to something new. Today the term may be used in a variety of contexts, as in biology and geology, but originally it was restricted with reference to the craft of the carpenter and the builder, who indeed in ancient Greek was called *tekton*.

When, in the early nineteenth century, neoclassicism brought an increased concern for a better understanding of Greek architecture, tectonics was one of the concepts that was discussed at length and consequently given greater depth and precision of meaning. A meaning, incidentally, which had been well understood in earlier architectural theory even though it was then linked to a different terminology. In French seventeenth- and eighteenth-century writing, authors would speak of the need to give a building visual qualities capable of convincing a viewer about its solidity, and in this sense *vraisemblance* (plausibility) became an important criterion. *"Ce n'est point assez de rendre un édifice solide,*

il faut que le jugement l'éstime tel" (It is not enough to make a building solid, judgment must estimate it as such), as one critic put it.[1]

Around the middle of the nineteenth century two German architects and theorists of stature published books which had the word "tectonic" in their titles: both Karl Boetticher[2] and Gottfried Semper[3] treated as a key problem the relation of final and expressive architectural forms to prototypes born from technological, constructional necessity. However, the fruitful discussion which had its start here was to remain incomplete until the ancient belief in a direct relation between man and the forms of architecture (Vitruvius, Book IV, Chapter 1) was splendidly corroborated by

Fig. 1. Detail of the Greek Doric Order, Parthenon, Athens. *(Photo Dolf Schnebli)*

Fig. 2. Late Gothic Ribbed Vault, Parish Church, Ybbsitz, Austria. *(Photo Dr. Walter Wagner.)*

psychological investigations and the concept of *Einfuehlung* (empathy) was formulated and elaborated by a number of scholars, among them Theodor Lipps.[4]

Empathy is one operating concept in Heinrich Wölfflin's brilliant early analyses of architecture and works of art to which all later writings on the topic owe such a gigantic debt. In his dissertation of 1886, significantly entitled *Prolegomena zu einer Psychologie der Architektur* (Prolegomena toward a Psychology of Architecture),[5] he recognized tectonics as the particular manifestation of empathy in the field of architecture. He asked himself: *"Wie koennen tektonische Formen Ausdruck sein?"* (How can tectonic forms be expressive?); he found the following explanation: *"Das Bild unserer selbst schieben wir allen Erscheinungen unter."* (We supposit our own image under all appearances.) Fourteen years later Geoffrey Scott expressed the same thought in words familiar to most English-speaking architects: "We have transcribed ourselves into terms of architecture."[6] In exploding what he called the "mechanical fallacy" in architectural criticism he made an extremely clear and convincing distinction between construction and tectonics, but failed to distinguish with equal clarity between construction and structure.

While Scott has the merit of having transmitted the ideas of Wölfflin and Lipps together with his own lucid observations to a wide circle of English-speaking readers, we owe a more recent debt for a similar service to Sir Herbert

Fig. 3. Masjid-i-Jami, Isfahan, Western Liwan, seen from the courtyard. *(Photo Friedrich Pfeil)*

Fig. 4. Masjid-i-Jami, Isfahan, Western Liwan, seen from the rear. *(Photo Dolf Schnebli)*

Read. He drew attention to the writings of two other scholars who are extremely relevant in our context, Wilhelm Worringer and Conrad Fiedler.

Worringer, in his dissertation of 1906,[7] opposed the concept of empathy to that of abstraction and, illustrating his argument, arrived at well characterized descriptions of tectonic expression in architecture but also at some generalizations which have been criticized.[8] Fiedler, whose writings date from around 1875, became most important for the understanding of twentieth-century art through having introduced the concept of "pure visibility."[9] His thinking enables us now to recognize tectonic expression as one result of that universal artistic activity which Paul Klee called "making visible"[10]) and which for Fiedler was but one manifestation of a more general mental activity which he described as "taking possession spiritually."[11]

Through tectonics the architect may make visible, in a strong statement, that intensified kind of experience of reality which is the artist's domain—in our case the experience of forces related to forms in a building. Thus structure, the intangible concept, is realized through construction and given visual expression through tectonics.

Discussions of visual phenomena should not remain abstract. Three well known examples may serve to illustrate the argument.

Fig. 5. Mies van der Rohe, corner detail from 860 Lake Shore Drive, Chicago. *(Photo Ben Weese)*

Fig. 6. Mies van der Rohe, corner detail from 2801 Commonwealth, Chicago. *(Photo Ben Weese)*

The Greek Doric temple never ceases to move us as an architectural experience (Fig. 1). Yet every beginning student of architecture knows today that its structural system of post-and-lintel, taken over from earlier timber prototypes, is ill suited to execution in stone—a material that does not lend itself to use in bending. Moreover as far as construction is concerned, few procedures can be more laborious and inefficient than to join together, carefully and without mortar, stones that had to be cut with extreme precision and, in many cases, had to be given their final complicated shape *in situ*. Yet who would apply criticism today in these terms when confronted with the reality of Paestum or the Parthenon? Obviously what matters, apart from other factors which are outside the scope of the present essay, is the tectonic statement: the noble gesture which makes visible a play of forces, of load and support in column and entablature, calling forth our own empathetic participation in the experience.

Similarly, we have learned that in the experience of a Gothic church it is the tectonic statement which shares with space and light the task of conveying an anagogical meaning.[12] In order to direct the beholder's mind spiritually upward, a play of forces is enacted most dramatically and appeals directly through empathy, even though what goes on behind the scenes of ribbing and shafting may be different from what we are led to believe (Fig. 2). In

Fig. 7. Mies van der Rohe, corner detail from 2400 Lake View Drive, Chicago. *(Photo Ben Weese)*

Fig. 8. Mies van der Rohe, corner detail from 1 Charles Center, Baltimore. *(Photo E. F. Sekler)*

retrospect it is not difficult to see how a great deal of effort expended in the fairly recent polemical discussion of Viollet-le-Duc's argument about "medieval rationalism"[13] in Gothic architecture might have been saved, had a conceptual framework prevailed in which structure, construction and tectonics were clearly distinguished.

Perhaps the most convincing visual demonstration of the difference between structure, construction and tectonics that could be wished is provided by the ensemble of a great Persian mosque such as the Masjid-i-Jami in Isfahan. Standing inside the courtyard and facing one of the liwans—a high vaulted niche with a door in the center—the structural principle is immediately apparent (Fig. 3): arch and vault are exploited in a fashion as magnificent as in the Gothic cathedral, but the tectonic expression is entirely different. The tectonics here depend not only on the great arch-form but equally on the geometry of the ceramic surfaces which frame the arch and on the vaulting which seems to hang from the soffit of the arch, rather than to support it. What comes as a real shock, however, is a revelation of the rear of the same liwan (Fig. 4), when suddenly the world of construction—the agglomeration of brick arches and buttresses—becomes apparent which seems to have little in common with the architectural expression in front.

Our discussion could be extended to many more examples and we would find an amazing richness in the way in which our three concepts may enter new combinations. The actual construction may militate against the structural principle, as in those examples from early civilizations where forms were translated from pliable materials into stone. The tectonic expression may be deliberately unclear, leaving a beholder marvelling at vast expanses of matter hovering apparently without effort over a void, as in so many Byzantine churches. There may be a tectonic negation created with the aid of atectonic forms which tend to disturb the viewer, as in Mannerist architecture; and there may even be a tectonic overstatement of what once was a simple constructional device, as in the elaborate bracketing that is a chief feature of Japanese monumental architecture.

But finally there are those rare cases when a building is an almost perfect realization of a structural principle in terms of a most appropriate and efficient construction while, at the same time, a clearly related unequivocal tectonic expression is found. At one end of the scale such buildings may occur in anonymous architecture, as in the corrugated, beehive-shaped mud huts of the Mousgoum tribe from Lake Tchad, so often illustrated in recent years.[14] At the other end of the scale there are such magnificent realizations as some of Torroja's buildings and Nervi's exhibition hall at Torino which illustrates what he himself called a "synthesis of static-aesthetic sensitivity, technical knowledge and mastery of execution."[15] In this description mastery of execution obviously stands for "construction" in our terminology, while technical knowledge may be related to "structure," and static-aesthetic sensitivity to empathy and thus to "tectonics." Torroja's and Nervi's work is also excellently suited to remind us of the simple truth that powerful tectonic expression need not be tied to a system which recalls the interplay of verticality and horizontality that goes with post-and-lintel.

Erich Mendelsohn must have recognized this at an early stage of his career when he wrote *"Die Beziehungen zwischen Tragen und Lasten—diese scheinbar fuer immer feststehenden Gesetze —werden auch ihr Bild umdeuten muessen . . ."* (The relations between support and load—these laws apparently fixed forever—will also have to re-evaluate their image . . .).[16]

Great architects have always handled the elements of tectonic expression with extreme care and untiring imagination, whether they were aware of it or not. When Frank Lloyd Wright explained the form of his Unitarian Church, Madison, Wisconsin, by placing his hands together as in prayer, illustrating "the expression of reverence and aspiration . . ." he was not demonstrating structure but tectonics.[17] Similarly, what so often is referred to erroneously as a concern with excellent construction in the *oeuvre* of Mies van der Rohe, turns out to be, on closer inspection, tectonic expressiveness refined to an extreme degree. A comparison of the ways in which he has handled corner-piers in a sequence of buildings will bear out the truth of this assertion, for we find variations which have but little structural or constructional justification but which are most telling tectonically (Figs. 5-8). A comparable study of Le Corbusier's concrete supports in a series of buildings also discloses a revealing variety of profiles which cannot be explained by structural or constructional reasons alone but which as far as tectonic expression goes is a "pure creation of his spirit" meant to provoke "plastic emotions."[18]

Among our three related concepts tectonics is the one most autonomously architectural; which is to say the architect may not be able to control the conditions of structure and construction as completely as he would like to, but he is the undisputed master of tectonic expression. Here his performance assuredly can be discussed on his own terms, and his artistic personality and character will manifest themselves most clearly.

Accordingly, in architectural criticism tectonics would seem to deserve as much consideration as some of the other elements which have been singled out for special discussion, chief among them space. It will be important however to remember that whatever is singled out, is isolated by a deliberate act of the critic for purposes of analysis; to speak of architecture in terms of tectonics alone would be as one-sided as to speak of it in terms of space alone. Just as the findings of psychology have moved from isolating such comparatively simple single explanations as "empathy" toward and beyond the complexities of interpreting *"Gestalt"* as a whole, architectural criticism also has to move in the direction of interpreting architectural experience as a totality. Both in creating and judging architecture those attempts will be most successful which are nourished from and return to a fullness of being that is no longer wholly subject to conscious control or completely amenable to intellectual analysis.

1. La Font de Saint Yenne and Ch.-E. Briseux, *Examen d'un Essai sur l'architecture*, Paris (1754) p. 47, quoted in Emil Kaufmann, "Die Architekturtheorie d. franzoesischen Klassik etc.," *Repertorium fuer Kunstwissenschaft*, XLIV (1924) p. 212.
2. Karl Boetticher, *Die Tektonik der Hellenen*, Potsdam (1852).
3. Gottfried Semper, *Der Stil in den technischen und tektonischen Kuensten*, Brunswick (1861), Munich (1863); 2nd edition Munich (1879).
4. According to Vernon Lee (*Beauty and Ugliness etc.*, London (1912) p. 20) the translation of "Einfuehlung" as empathy is due to Edward Titchener who used it in his *Psychology of Thought Processes*, London (1909) six years after the first volume of Theodor Lipps' *Aesthetik* had appeared.
5. Reprinted in: Heinrich Wölfflin, *Kleine Schriften*, Bâle (1946).
6. Geoffrey Scott, *The Architecture of Humanism*, 2nd ed., London (1924) p. 213. The author refers to Wölfflin in his preface and to Lipps in a footnote on p. 213. For a discussion of Scott's relation to Lippsian theory see Reyner Banham, *Theory and Design in the First Machine Age*, London (1960) p. 67.
7. *Abstraction and Empathy*, Worringer's dissertation was published as a book in 1908; an English translation by M. Bullock was published in New York in 1953.
8. Ernst H. Gombrich, *Art and Illusion*, New York (1960) p. 21; Meyer Schapiro, "Style", in *Anthropology Today*, ed. A. L. Kroeber, Chicago (1953).
9. Werner Hofmann, "Studien zur Kunsttheorie des 20. Jahrhunderts," *Zeitschrift f. Kunstgeschichte*, XVIII (1955) p. 136.
10. *Paul Klee: The Thinking Eye*, J. Spiller ed., London (1961) p. 76.
11. Conrad Fiedler, "Bemerkungen ueber Wesen und Geschichte der Baukunst," *Deutsche Rundschau*, XV (1878) p. 361 ff.
12. Erwin Panofsky, *Meaning in the Visual Arts*, Garden City, N. Y. (1955) p. 128; Otto von Simson, *The Gothic Cathedral*, New York (1956) p. 6; Paul Frankl, *The Gothic etc.*, Princeton (1960).
13. Pol Abraham, *Viollet-le-Duc et le rationalisme mediéval*, Paris (1934).
14. *L'habitat au Cameroun*, Paris (1952) p. 33.
15. *The Works of Pier Luigi Nervi*, London (1957) preface.
16. Erich Mendelsohn, *Briefe eines Architekten*, O. Beyer ed., Munich (1961) p. 27.
17. *Frank Lloyd Wright: Writings and Buildings*, selected by Edgar Kaufmann and Ben Raeburn, New York (1960) p. 168.
18. Le Corbusier, *Towards a New Architecture*, transl. F. Etchells, London (1927) p. 11.

PIER LUIGI NERVI   IS ARCHITECTURE MOVING TOWARD UNCHANGEABLE FORMS?

During these past few years many discussions have developed on the theme of the relationship between architectural form and the technological possibilities due to new materials, such as reinforced concrete, steel, and in general to our expanded technical and building knowledge.

The two extremes to which the opposite trends have limited themselves: on one hand the negation of the technical fact as a possible means of architectural expressivity, and on the other hand the super-evaluation of it, both seem to me to miss the point. It is not that architecture must follow the possibilities offered by steel or reinforced concrete, nor that these possibilities are in themselves a means of architectural inspiration, but certainly these materials are, or can be, more suitable to express the ideas and sentiments of our time, of which the eminently technical and mechanical atmosphere cannot be ignored.

From my point of view, however, the most important and determining factor for the architectural and constructional tendencies of today and tomorrow is given by certain absolute elements which technical progress, and above all the requirements of aero-dynamics have established, and which are stable and unchangeable within the continuous fluctuation of the tastes and aesthetic aspirations of man.

In fact, I would say that humanity is heading toward forms, and perhaps toward a "style" which, once reached, will forever remain unchanged and unchangeable in time. This affirmation may seem rather risky, but it is based on facts so uncontestable that it must at least be considered seriously.

Without a doubt the aesthetic tastes of man start from a few isolated points and from there expand step by step into all creative fields, not only the artistic and architectural ones, but also the technical and functional ones. In this manner we see that the horse-drawn carriages, ships, palaces, furniture, fittings, decorative objects and even the clothing of a certain era are in perfect accord with one another, and that they all are pervaded with a certain character difficult to define but which is called style.

It is certainly difficult to explain precisely the profound reasons why these predominant characteristics have successively evolved and modified themselves. There is, however, no doubt that ever since mankind learned to exceed the speed of 60 miles per hour, to build airplanes, to construct suspension bridges spanning 3000 feet, arches spanning over 300, and buildings many hundred feet high, he has introduced into his environment absolute and eternal laws which have materialized in forms and structures intimately tied to everyday life.

The forms for minimum resistance to movement, fundamental for all fast vehicles, and literally the reason for the existence of airplanes, do not, in fact, depend on the taste of the designer or on his aesthetic aspirations, but are determined by physical laws which are valid for all people and all time.

I read some time ago that to define more accurately the forms for minimum resistance to movement for automobile bodies, a builder resorted to models of ice placed in a current of air which directly modified and corrected the models, melting the various points according to their greater or lesser resistance to the current, and producing the desired result.

Where can one find a more impersonal and unchangeable molding process?

How can one imagine that the result obtained today will not be exactly the same as that arrived at in any point on earth and at any time, even in the most distant foreseeable future?

It must be added that the purely mechanical development of certain activities, such as that of fast transportation, has created constructional themes of great dimensions and of great technical re-

Pier Luigi Nervi. Collaborating engineer: Aldo Arcangeli. Gatti Wool Factory, Rome, 1953. View of basement. The ceiling is constructed of slabs of Ferro–cemento. The pattern of the ribs follows the isostatic lines of the principal bending moments, "a design which makes possible strict adherence to the laws of statics, and therefore makes the most efficient use of the materials . . . The aesthetically satisfying result . . . is a clear reminder of the mysterious affinity to be found between physical laws and our own senses."

sponsibility, which remain strictly tied to solutions that follow the laws of statics.

A road built only for animal traffic could climb over hills and descend again, with tight turns, to the bottom of the valley, reducing the span of bridges to the mere width of the water course; the weights to be supported were limited to a few thousand pounds; access ramps, and even the actual road bed, could have very steep slopes and limited width.

With the railroads, the present-day expressways, and even more the railroads and expressways of tomorrow, elevated roadways and bridges of great span become necessary, while the weights to be supported climb to many hundred tons.

At the same time the need arises for buildings of great constructional importance for railroad stations, airplane hangars, office buildings, sports palaces, all problems which are decisively and unquestionably dominated by statics which determines the solution in harmony with laws as unchangeable as the other physical laws.

Therefore, while the arch of a bridge of limited span, or even more of a door or a window, could be designed arbitrarily and could follow the aesthetic tendencies of the moment, the arch of great span, the covering for a vast interior space, the structure having to resist great weights, all must have forms that are well defined and fixed beforehand by nature, no matter what the aesthetic tendency of their designer may be.

The number of works which, having reached the natural form, will have to stick to it forever, will therefore increase step by step until in a few decades they will reach such importance that they will become a decisive, directing force and produce a truly stylistic character of their own.

In fact, we can observe that the aerodynamic forms necessary for fast vehicles, but absolutely superfluous for slow ones, have already formed our tastes to such a degree that any vehicle—from a heavy truck to a baby carriage—appears decidedly ugly to us unless it conforms in some way to, or has some characteristic element of, that style.

This is particularly true with buildings: when the dimensions of the work or the static necessities are very important, the perfect adherence to the most natural and spontaneous static laws, besides being necessary because of technical and economical reasons, is a fundamental element in the aesthetic satisfaction of that building.

There exists in everyone, even if unconsciously, an instinctive sensibility which is not, and cannot be, satisfied if a work of great statical importance does not follow, in an evident manner, the fundamental laws of equilibrium of weight and mass.

I have tried to draw two schemes for a bridge, one with an arch of approximately elliptical profile, and the other with a profile that corresponded to the funicular curve of the weights and which approached a parabola.

The curve of the first, taken by itself as a pure geometric fact, is without doubt as harmonious and satisfying as the second, but as soon as we add its statical characteristic of holding up the weight of the roadway, its unnatural character becomes obvious.

The architect who, violating the most elementary laws of economy of construction, should succeed in building such a structure, wasting steel and concrete to overcome the stresses due to the illogical profile of the arch, would in fact be committing an aesthetic error as well as a technical one.

98

Pier Luigi Nervi. Municipal Stadium, Florence, finished 1932.
View showing fork-shaped constructions through which are distributed the forces of the cantilevered beams of the stadium roof.

Pier Luigi Nervi. Exposition Hall, Turin. View of interior of Salone B, 243' x 310', 1948–49. The semi-circular apse has a diameter of 131'. The corrugated vault of the roof, which spans 240', is constructed of prefabricated units of Ferro–cemento. The fan-shaped buttresses at the sides of the hall, also of Ferro–cemento, gather in the forces from the arch of the roof.

Let it be added, finally, that whenever the constructional problem exceeds certain dimensions, the greatest ingenuity of the designer will not be able to move it from the road of the strictest obedience to the laws of statics; an arch bridge of three hundred or more foot span will have today, tomorrow and always, the same profile determined by the funicular of the weights, nor will any human desire be able to change it.

Buildings for habitation obviously remain freer.

No law of statics will oppose the construction of a building that follows any of the stylistic characteristics of the past or those which fantasy might create in the future.

However, even wanting artificially to neglect the influence which the well defined examples I have previously indicated will have on such building, one can perceive even today certain forces of social and economic nature that will guide the building industry toward a structural and decorative moderation and clarity which will be in good harmony with the purity of form of the work that is mainly of technical importance.

In any case, the problems of urban planning will remain completely free, and may create new and great architectural developments.

One can imagine a city of tomorrow in which the residential buildings (once the extreme, arrogant ostentation of the aristocratic palace of the past or the pitiable pretentiousness of most of the buildings of today has been abandoned) will assume a limpid, clear and honest constructional sincerity, made lively and gay by well studied relationships between streets, plazas and gardens. The eminently architectural and monumental character will be reserved to the few buildings of public or representative use, which will be the origin of the highest and most significant expressions of the new architecture, as were at one time the princely palaces.

Faced with this evident intervention of material and technical elements in fields which up till today apparently had remained the uncontested domain of the mind, one might fear an impairment of those poetic and sentimental factors which constitute the most precious heritage of humanity.

However, excluding the possibility that an accentuation of the change that has taken place in the past hundred years in the intellectual capacity of man (how else can one explain the recent prodigious technical development and the fact that every uncultured person of today has physical and mechanical conceptions and sensibilities superior to the most learned man of the past), might bring such revolutionary and unforeseen transformations as to affect the very roots of our being, I maintain that the fear of a spiritual impoverishment because of technology is absolutely unfounded.

To approach the mysterious laws of nature with modest aspirations and to try to interpret and command them by obeying them, is the only method to bring their majestic eternity to the service of our limited and contingent goals. This, in itself, has profound poetry which can be translated into forms of the highest artistic and aesthetic expression.

One can truly imagine a civilization of tomorrow served and guided by a technology which will no longer be exclusively an arid means to achieve riches for individuals or for certain peoples, or even worse, an inhuman warlike and destroying power, but will mean an intelligent use of the energy and resources of the physical world, and above all, will be the cause and consequence of man's increasingly intimate closeness to the divine wisdom of the creation.

a

Pier Luigi Nervi. Collaborating urban planner: Marcello Piacentini. Palazzo dello Sport, Rome, 1958–59.
a: View of ceiling. The ribs are constructed of prefabricated units of Ferro–cemento, and curve outward to a 300′ tension ring at the perimeter of the seating section.
b: View showing 8 of the 48 prefabricated pilasters beneath the ring surrounding the seating section. Through these pilasters are transmitted the forces from the ribs of the ceiling.

b

The equilibrium and harmony that reign over technology, the objectivity that one is forced to assume in its presence, the modesty that its unplumbed mysteries demand of us, constitute such an elegant lesson that it cannot but have profound repercussions on all intellectual and moral manifestations and even on the life of society.

The progressive refinement of the capacity to understand and to perceive by intuition the physical laws will make ever more evident the intrinsic and pure beauty of the forms answering the necessity of a technology in constant development; many purely imaginative or capricious fashions of mankind will be stifled from the start, all activities will tend to group themselves in the logical mentality of good rendition and equilibrium which dominates all correct technical solutions.

Nor must one fear that the adoption of forms and volumes closely following natural laws must lead to a monotonous and unsupportable uniformity of products.

Almost all of the present airplanes have reached profiles of least resistance, and although they all belong to a single category of form, they all show the different aesthetic sensibilities of their designers and the most specific characteristics of the tastes of the nations that produced them.

Even within the realm of the most rigorous technology, the mind remains and will remain completely free and able to express, interpret and manifest its most profound and mysterious creative forces.

The design process is fundamental for the creation of buildings and determines their form from the first preliminary studies when the architectural idea is born to the final construction phase where every structural element is studied in detail.

It can be defined broadly as the invention and study of the necessary methods to achieve a defined goal with maximum efficiency.

The concepts of what is the goal to be reached, and what are the most efficient means of reaching it, cannot be separated from the design process, and pinpoint and define the terms of the relative problems.

It would be senseless, in fact, to make a study which did not aim for an exact and concrete result, and which did not try to reach it with maximum efficiency, that is, a broadly defined efficiency not entirely limited by economic factors.

Even though the design process can vary, one can none-the-less state several fundamental laws directed at clarifying the start of the design and facilitating its development.

I maintain, in fact, that a correct architectural development is impossible unless one obeys and is guided by these premises of general character: a) A clear idea of the goal to be reached, and an understanding of the methods available to reach it. b) An absolute independence of mind with respect to solutions that have already been proposed for similar problems, or to fashions or present stylistic trends.

The clear, unperturbed and unperturbable view of the goal to be reached must be the constant guide during all the long and laborious design process.

In fact, it is impossible to obtain perfect functionalism in building unless both the general scheme and every part of it are subordinated from the very beginning to the ends it must serve.

Although this observation may seem so obvious as to appear superfluous if not banal, one can see everyday with how much facility these simple directives are neglected even in projects whose primary and fundamental aim is functional.

In fact, we have seen erected, with a huge waste of material and labor, railroad stations unsuited to traffic, sports and entertainment places with poor visibility or acoustics, bridges which hinder the flowing of rivers, roads which do not follow the necessity of city traffic, and in general buildings which do not serve the purposes for which they were built.

One cannot explain these serious errors except by admitting that, from the very start of the project, the designer let himself stray from the precise goal which the work had to meet.

The elementary nature of the functional incongruities which one finds in many constructions, even very important ones, excludes, in fact, the possibility that they can be the result of lack of competency in the problem or from a poor technical preparation.

It is perhaps not extraneous to observe that similar incongruities between the goals to be reached and the methods used to achieve them can also be found in other very important human activities and have caused grave consequences and disasters.

There are many examples of industrial, commercial or private activities, or even worse, of political developments and even wars, which were conducted in a manner so much at variance with the most natural one, as to show that those who directed had forgotten, along the way, the program with which they had started.

One can deduce, therefore, that to follow a well-defined objective with clear ideas and unchang-

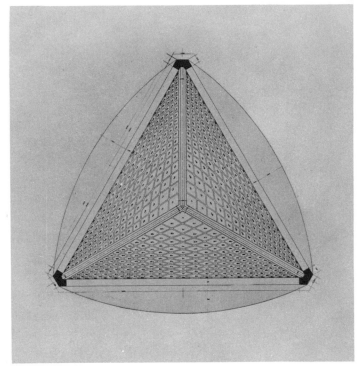

Pier Luigi Nervi. Collaborating architects: Antonio Nervi and Carlo Vannoni. Collaborating engineer: Francesco Vacchini. Project for Cathedral, New Norcia, Australia, 1959–61.
a: Model of roof structure: three parabolic vaults, approximately 100′ high, spanning 115′.
b: Plan of roof structure seen from below: triangular base 240′ on each side.

ing actions is, from a practical point of view, due to an intrinsic human weakness, far more difficult than one might think after a cursory examination of the problem.

None-the-less, one can observe that it is not enough to want decidedly to reach a goal; one must also be able to create the most useful and convenient methods to reach that goal, exploiting all circumstances.

The designer, therefore, must have a complete knowledge of all the conditions that limit each construction problem, and full command of the technical-constructional methods, as well as the correct planimetric distribution of spaces and their functional interdependence.

A complete command of technology is necessary and fundamental as a starting point for all architectural solutions that are to rise above the usual construction banalities.

In fact, to be able to decide the type of bridge, the size of special spaces, the possibility of whether or not to eliminate obstructing supports—all elements which are decisive in determining an architectural solution—the knowledge of the laws of statics and the real technological, constructional and economical possibilities, is absolutely necessary and indispensable.

One must also keep in mind that the study of planimetric distribution and of the most efficient correlation of spaces, of their number and dimensions, requires, especially for buildings of primarily functional nature, a knowledge so perfect of all aspects of the life that will take place in these buildings, that a true specialization becomes almost indispensable.

But the most necessary and indispensable condition for the correct development of a project is a mental attitude of complete freedom of mind with respect to solutions that have already been studied for similar problems, or to fashions and stylistic trends of the moment.

Problems in the building industry which at first may seem similar, are in fact always different in some particular, except in exceptional circumstances: a slight difference is enough to change some of the principal characteristics of the solution.

Whoever has studied even the simplest apartment plan knows from experience what radical changes in the distribution of all spaces is brought about by the displacement of any one space or by a variation, even small, of the dimensions or form of the available area.

In the study of a building, one must add to the problems of a planimetric character those of an ambiental nature, which, from the point of view of both style and construction, vary greatly from region to region.

On the other hand, planimetric or architectural changes whose aim is to make an already existing solution valid for the new problem, besides the labor and time this involves, always give results which are decidedly poor and incurably inorganic.

One can add, finally, that no solution is perfect, and that all projects, even those of the leading architects, can be improved and perfected. Therefore no solution can be accepted a priori.

The designer, then, must prepare himself for the difficult creative work with a mind completely free from all outside influence and even from recollections of his own solutions, having very clearly in mind only the following: an architectural idea; the terms of the problem; the technological, constructional and economical means to achieve it; the full realization of the responsibility connected with a creative act whose fruit will remain beyond his lifetime, forming a part, even if small, of that spiritual and material complex which one generation passes to the succeeding ones.

From these premises can start the work of sketching out structures and systemizing the spaces, of comparing them and choosing which merit further study. Only after the most difficult and passionate labor, this produces the final definition of the organism which best seems to fit the requirements.

No other creative act is so long and difficult because no other expressive language (words, sounds, colors, and sculptural forms) is as rebellious as the architectural one, formed as it is by limitations and ties of functional, statical, and constructional nature.

The most impassioned jump into fantasy comes up against cold reality and meets with imperatives and obstacles which must be overcome with compromises or adjustments; more than once, when a rather good solution seems to have been reached, an insurmountable technical, functional or economic difficulty comes up which makes it necessary to abandon what has already been done and instead try new approaches.

Until the time when function, statics and economy are brought together in an equilibrated compromise, and harmonize spontaneously with one another in a play of forms and volumes capable of expressing the architectural idea, the labor of the design process is not finished.

It is obvious that in this very labor the good designer will have to find the intimate and incomparable satisfaction that is connected with every creative act, a satisfaction which is greater the more difficult the problems are to overcome.

No monetary compensation, not even the hope of fame, would be a sufficient stimulus for such long and exhausting work.

If independence of mind is a good premise for the search for correct functional and constructional solutions, it becomes absolutely indispensable with regard to aesthetics.

The character of a building does not depend on the profile of the moulding, on the dimensions of the windows, or on some decorative detail, but on the fundamental relationships of volumes and forms, on the characteristics of the load bearing structure, in short, on elements that deal, not with the finish, but with the skeleton and structural organism of the building. To believe one is modernizing a building which was conceived in a spirit not permeated by truly new ideas and sentiments, is the same as the sterile and pitiable mistake of trying to make an old face look young with make-up and paint.

In fact, one can observe in our cities innumerable buildings finished with all the decorative formulary of the twentieth century style, which never-the-less, in their actual building forms, have all the same heaviness, banality and pretentiousness of many of their brethren constructed, for example, in the Umbertino or Liberty style. Probably the designers of these works would have achieved better results if, instead of starting with the supposition of creating something "modern," they had followed spontaneously, with a clear state of mind, the expression of their own constructional and aesthetic capacities, and especially their own natural inspiration, which, being inevitably influenced by those complex factors which form the society we live in, would have been a more effective expression of our time than could ever be a few decorative elements applied in order to follow the momentary fad rather than the intimate conviction.

Independence of mind is all the more indispensable, the more important the work is to be designed and the greater are the artistic capacities of the designer.

The highest prerogative of the artist is in fact that of being able to synthesize in a natural, and I would say almost involuntary manner, the characteristic sentiments of his own time and to translate them into forms valid for everyone.

It is obvious that this very delicate work of synthesis will succeed most effectively when there is the greatest possible freedom for the sensibilities and inspirations of the artist to manifest themselves in the most genuine and spontaneous manner.

It is difficult to think about the relationship between buildings except in conventional terms. What fills the mind's screen when it is asked to call up the idea of a building is a certain sort of lump next to a road: pretty well what any architect would have in mind since the onset of the individual building in the Seventies and Eighties of the last century—the time of those blockbusters of buildings illustrated in the *Builder* (beloved of Henry Russell Hitchcock); of engravings of railway stations, banks, villas and so on; of H. H. Richardson and Giles Gilbert Scott. Such architects were, of course, immensely inventive—these were on the whole new programs met head-on—but the urban build-up which resulted was either random ugly block (South Kensington, Museums) or organized big ugly block (Paris, Opera House), with pretty much of a wasteland in between.

Such a pattern had of course been seen before, in ancient Rome for example—the last time many new programs had been met head-on—this pattern had then disappeared with the collapse of mass needs. But an air photograph of downtown Los Angeles, or newly redeveloped (and fully town-planned) Rotterdam, shows the same big lumps unrelated even in the most obvious and literal sense one to another: roads and emptiness in between.

It is that emptiness that makes for the rapid car-enclosed dash from building to building, the venetian blinds on the windows, the interior decorator, and the feeling that there is nowhere to go.

This is a failure of architecture, of our mode of thinking about architecture, not something that can be laid at the feet of the client or the town planning bureau.

Fig. 1. Sheffield University Redevelopment Project.

Buildings should be thought of from the beginning as fragments; as containing within themselves a capacity to act with other buildings: they should be themselves links in systems. The only viable mode of city-structuring is for all to develop a sense of structure, for when a feeling of responsibility for the emergence of a structure is not there, an imposed structure cannot help (e.g. the residential quadratas of Brasilia).

The city as a big house lived in by us all, the sum of individual acts freely undertaken is a fine dream, but one not even fragmentarily possible unless the citizen realizes that it is the way he adds that garage to his house and how he shapes and disciplines himself, his children, his household objects, that shapes the neighborhood; and unless the architect relearns his discipline, so it can respond to that sort of realization.

Sheffield University Redevelopment Project

In this project, made in 1953, for the redevelopment of Sheffield University, we were faced with the usual urban problems: a large volume of buildings, to be put onto a small site, where there were existing buildings which had to be retained.

On the plan in Figure 2 the old buildings are shown in black and the new buildings are in gray. The new buildings make a sort of snake with a stick across its neck, the curled-up library being the tail, the public lecture halls the head. The disposition of the various parts is as follows:

1. Public lecture halls
2. Administration
3. Lecture halls
4. Faculty buildings
5. Library
6. Bridge, from library through old building and administration, across road to—
7. Social Facilities

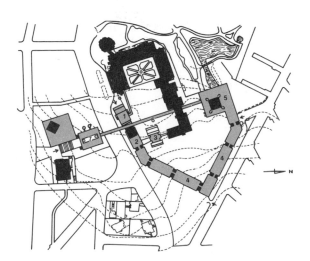

Fig. 2. Sheffield University Redevelopment Project.

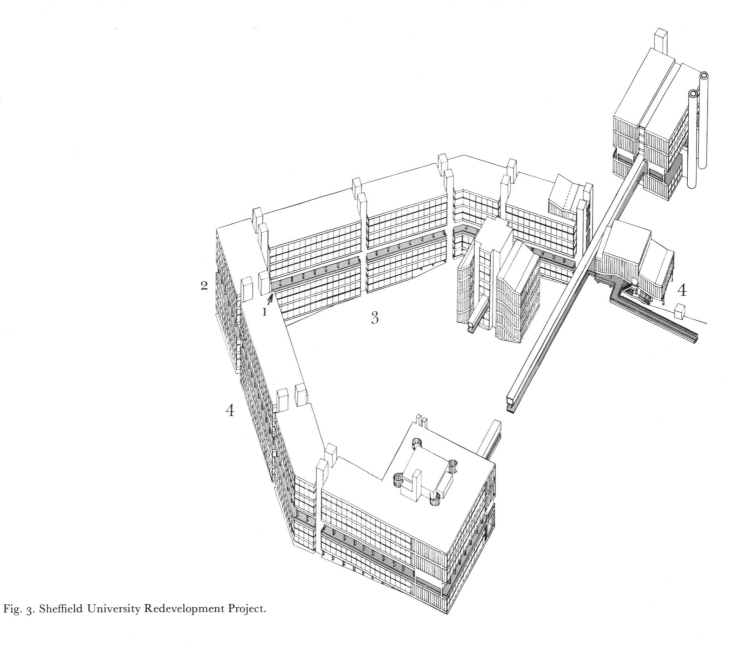

Fig. 3. Sheffield University Redevelopment Project.

Now what is special about all this is its handling of the means of circulation, the old buildings, the new accommodation, and the open spaces, to make one group structure far more useful and easy to use than could have been accomplished by the usual process of adding separate buildings each an island to itself. Figure 3 makes clear this handling of the means of circulation:

1. The pedestrian deck (indicated by stippling in the diagram) is not only a means of circulation, but also a social space, a place for notice boards, etc.

2. Here the building grows higher as ground slopes away, but reasonable access is maintained to all parts from the pedestrian deck.

3. Green space, not used for routine circulation, is therefore available for sitting on the grass (it runs into an adjacent public park), or being hailed from the deck.

4. All servicing takes place around the periphery and does not interfere with other systems. Figure 1 shows the long bridge links new and old buildings, and crosses the main highway in a dramatic and memorable fashion.

This is what I call a non-building building—a demonstration of a new way of thinking about urban construction—in which the parts build towards the group.

Conventionally offices are like houses with a bigger door. This door is also the symbolic point of entry—the point to which we are naturally drawn. Through that door now try to pass motorcars, bicycles, scooters and 1000 work people on foot. Often we can not even get near. The big door has offered us false hope of entry. But its aim was correct: to provide a readily comprehended message, "Come in here."

We have now to evolve means of organization and a language of equal obviousness for the new situations, "Here I must walk in," "Here leave my car," "This way deliver the new machines," as in Figure 4 for example.

The problem is the same in the housing area, but the need for quietude, which has been provided for in the office area, is even greater here.

Conventionally housing areas are made by putting house with house in such a way that they add little to each other. (Where there are relatively few houses and much open space, this criticism obviously does not apply. In such areas—Camberley, New Canaan, Santa Barbara, Drottingholm—the "structure" is largely one of trees and roads; houses as such play a very small part.) This conventional arrangement has been totally compromised by the motorcar; the front garden destroyed, the children in danger. But alternatives in which the means of circulation, the open space, and the house proper are thought of as one thing, are possible, as for example the plans shown in Figure 5.

What I regard as old-fashioned about the ideas I have put forward here is that they are concerned with building as one operation (or series of consecutive operations) by one directing authority. But in its purest sense the ideal of "building towards the community structure" as the natural way of building, is a new and very demanding ideal. We have to learn to see the town as the sum of individual acts, develop disciplines so these primarily self-serving acts can serve also collective ends.

Fig. 4. "Community Structured" Office Area.

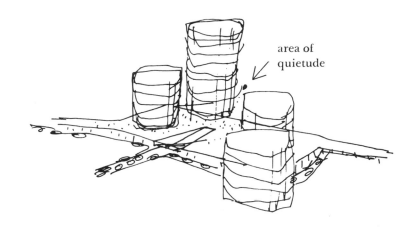

area of
quietude

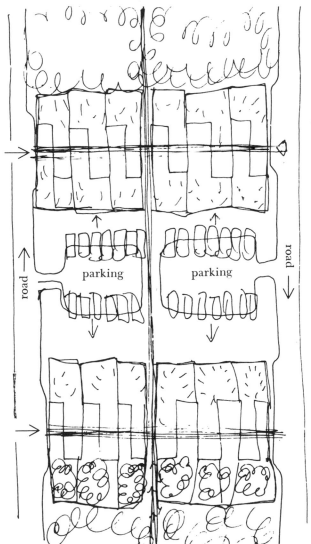

quietude

covered
pedestrian
access

houses
& yards

road

road

parking

parking

houses
& yards

covered
pedestrian
access

Fig. 5. "Community Structured" Housing Area.

quietude

There is no more critically concerned observer of our rapidly changing society than the urban designer. Charged with giving form—with perceiving and contributing order—to agglomerates of buildings, highways and greenspaces in which men have increasingly come to work and live, the urban designer stands between technology and human need and seeks to make the first a servant, for the second must be paramount in a civilized world.

In what follows, we shall discuss three ways of thinking about the plural forms of the city, and how they are composed. Segments of the total form of the city will be referred to as "collective form". Three means for establishing collective forms—three compositional methods—will be discussed. For the moment, we are designers only, interested in technology and order, insofar as these may be divorced from the political and the economic.

Of course, the progenitors of any formal idea include politics and economics. The reason, in fact, for searching for new formal concepts in contemporary cities lies in the magnitude of relatively recent change in those very problems. Our urban society is characterized by: (1) coexistence and conflict of amazingly heterogeneous institutions and individuals; (2) unprecedently rapid and extensive transformations in the physical structure of the society; (3) rapid and complex communications methods and (4) technological progress and its impact upon regional cultures.

The force of these contemporary urban characteristics makes it impossible to visualize urban form as did Roman military chiefs, or Renaissance architects such as Sangallo and Michelangelo; nor can we easily perceive a hierarchical order as did many theorists in town planning in the quite recent past. We must now see our urban society as a dynamic field of interrelated forces. It is a set of mutually independent variables in a rapidly expanding infinite series. Any order introduced within the pattern of forces contributes to a state of dynamic equilibrium—an equilibrium which will change in character as time passes.

Thus our concern here is not a "master plan", but a "master program", since the latter term includes a time dimension. Given a set of goals, the "master program" suggests several alternatives for achieving them, the use of one or another of which is decided by the passage of time and its effect on the ordering concept.

As a physical correlate of the master program, there are "master forms" which differ from buildings in that they, too, respond to the dictates of time.

Our problem is this: Do we have in urban design adequate

Fig. 1. Medieval Italian Town: San Gimignano, distant view. *(Photo Courtesy Italian State Tourist Office)*

Fig. 2. Greek Island Town: Amorgas, Cyclades. *(Photo Courtesy Royal Greek Embassy Press and Information Service)*

Fig. 3. Horyuji, Japan.
(*Photo Futagawa*)

visual language with which we can create and organize space within the master program? Cities today tend to be visually and physically confused. They are monotonous patterns of static elements. They lack visual and physical character consonant with the functions and technology which compose them. They also lack elasticity and flexibility. Our cities must change as social and economic use dictate, and yet they must not be "temporary" in the worst visual sense.

We lack an adequate visual language to cope with the superhuman scale of modern highway systems and with views from airplanes. The visual and physical concepts at our disposal have to do with single buildings, and with closed compositional means for organizing them.

Certain historical examples of town-building have become interesting to urban designers recently because they appear to be useful and suggestive examples of collective form: medieval Italian towns such as San Gimignano (Fig. 1), towns of the Greek islands (Fig. 2), or villages in French Africa are a few examples. The spatial and compositional quality of these towns is worth consideration.

Factors which determine the spatial organization of these towns are these:

1. Consistent use of basic materials and construction methods, as well as spontaneous but minor variations in physical expression.

2. Wise and often dramatic use of geography and topography.

3. Human scale preserved throughout the town. (This is frequently in contrast to superhuman land forms.)

4. Finally, sequential development[1] of basic elements which are predominantly dwelling-houses, open spaces between the houses, and the repetitive use of certain visual elements such as walls, gates, towers, etc.

The sequential form in historical examples developed over a period of time much longer than that in which contemporary cities are being built and rebuilt. In this sense the efforts of contemporary urban designers are quite different from their historical counterparts, and the forms which they consciously evolve in a short time span must accordingly differ.

Three design approaches to collective form may be distinguished. The first of these, the *compositional* approach, is an historical one. The second two (*megastructure* and *group-form*) are new, and are efforts toward finding master forms which satisfy the demands of contemporary urban growth and change.

117

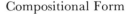

Compositional Form

The compositional approach is a commonly accepted and practiced concept at this moment. Generally the design process is divided into two stages: First, there is a functional diagram. This is rarely done in three dimensions. Next, the individually tailored buildings are composed following the functional diagram, with or without linkage.

Most contemporary housing schemes and urban renewal projects fall into this category. Rockefeller Center, Chandigarh, Brasilia, or Horyuji (Fig. 3) are good examples of compositional urban design. The compositional approach is used in conjunction with classical concepts of the master plan.

This is a still valid approach in many cases. It may, however, tend to widen a discrepancy between evolving social organism and its physical statement, because the expression and growth pattern of the group of buildings are limited by those of each individual building, which is static and complete in itself.

The compositional approach is a familiar one, and it has received exhaustive treatment in numerous works on architecture and planning. We will, therefore, let it stand on its merits, and introduce two less well-known approaches to the problem of urban design.

Megastructure

The megastructure is a large frame in which all the functions of a city or part of a city are housed. It has been made possible by present-day technology. In a sense, it is a man-made feature of the landscape. It is like the great hill on which Italian towns were built.

Urban designers are attracted to the megastructure concept because it offers a legitimate way to order massive grouped functions. One need only to have looked at work in the exhibition of "Visionary Architecture" at the Museum of Modern Art, New York (September–December, 1960), to sense the excitement generated among designers by megaform. While some of the ideas displayed in the exhibition demonstrated structural virtuosity at the expense of human scale and human functional needs, others had a quality which suggested no divergence between compacted, economic function and human use.

One of the most interesting developments of the megaform has been suggested by Kenzo Tange in connection with his Tokyo Bay Project (Fig. 4). He presents a proposal for a mass-human scale form which includes a megaform and discrete, rapidly changeable functional units which fit within the larger framework. He reasons that short-lived items are becoming more and more short-lived, and the cycle of change is shrinking at a corresponding rate. On the other hand, the accumulation of capital has made it possible to build in large-scale operations. Reformations of natural topography, dams, harbors, and highways are of a size and scope that involve long cycles of time, and these are the man-made works that tend to divide the overall system of the age. "The two tendencies—toward shorter cycles and toward longer cycles—are both necessary to modern life and to humanity itself."[2]

This megaform concept depends largely upon the idea that change will occur less rapidly in some realms than it will in others, and that the designer will be able to ascertain which of the functions he is dealing with fall in the long cycle of change, and which in the shorter. The question is, can the designer successfully base his concept on the idea that, for example, transportation methods will change less rapidly than the idea of a desirable residence or retail outlet? Sometimes, the impact and momentum of technology become so great that a change occurs in the basic skeleton of social and physical structure. It is difficult to predict to which part of the pond a stone will be thrown and which way the ripples will spread. If the megaform becomes rapidly obsolete, as well it might, especially in those schemes which do not allow for two kinds of change cycle, it will be a great weight about the neck of urban society.

On the other hand, the ideal is not a system in which the physical structure of the city is at the mercy of unpredictable change. The ideal is a kind of master form which can move into ever new states of equilibrium and yet maintain visual consistency and a sense of continuing order in the long run.

Inherent in the megastructure concept, along with a certain static nature, is the suggestion that many and diverse functions may beneficially be concentrated in one place. A large frame implies some utility in combination and concentration of function.

That utility, however, is sometimes only apparent. We frequently confuse the potential that technology offers with a kind of compulsion to "use it fully". Technological possibility can be sanguinely useful only when it is a tool of civilized persons. Inhuman use of technological advance is all too frequently our curse. Optimum productivity does not even depend on mere concentration of activities and workers.

Technology must not dictate choices to us in our cities. We must learn to select modes of action from among the possibilities technology presents in physical planning.

If the megastructure concept presents the problems outlined above, it also has great promise for:

1. Environmental engineering: Megastructure development necessitates collaboration between structural engineer and civil engineer. Possibilities in large spans, space frames, light skin structures, prestressed concrete, highway aesthetics, and earth forming will be developed far beyond their present level. Large scale climatic control will be studied further. A new type of physical structure, neither architecture nor civil engineering, but a noble environmental building will emerge.

2. Multi-functional structure: We have, thus far, taken it for granted that buildings should be designed to fulfill one specific purpose. In spite of the fact that, as indicated above, the concept of multi-functionalism must be approached with caution, it offers useful possibilities. We can, within the megaform structure, realize combinations such as those in Noriaki Kurokawa's "Agricultural City" (Fig. 5).

Fig. 4. Kenzo Tange. Tokyo Bay Project: Model of a Community for 25,000. *(Photo Kawazoe)*

Fig. 5. Noriaki Kurokawa. Model of Agricultural City. *(Photo E. Torihata)*

Group-Form

Group-form is the second of collective form ideas. It is a form which evolves from a *system of generative elements* in space.

Traditionally, human activities, attitudes toward beauty, feelings about space and techniques in construction have evolved the styles which mark the history of man's aesthetic search. Each of the historical styles had a form, or a concept of form as its substructure.

The human quality which determines form has to do with way of life, movement, and relation of persons in mass society. Group-form is an effort to create a new total image in order to express the vitality of our society, at the same time embracing individuality and retaining the identity of individual elements. It is worth noting that group-form evolves generally from the people of a society rather than from its powerful leadership. It is the village, the dwelling group, and the bazaar, which are group-form in the sense we are using this term, and not the palace complex, which is compositional in character.

The idea of the responsiveness of forms in group-form has been seen by John Voelker, in his CIAM Team X report, in the context of an "open aesthetics." He comments that "in an open aesthetics, form is a master key, . . . capable of reciprocating the constant change of life. . . . Open aesthetics is the living extension of functionalism."[3]

Forms in group-form have their own link, whether expressed or latent, so that they may grow in a system. They define basic environmental spaces which also partake of the quality of systematic linkage. Group-form and its spaces are *prototype elements*, and they are prototypical because of implied system and linkage.

The elements and the system are reciprocal, both in design and in operation. The elements suggest a system, and that, in turn, demands further development of the elements, in a kind of feedback system.

Though geometry is a tool of the search for group-form, it is not an end in itself. One cannot seek group-form in hexagons, triangles, and circles, in Neoplatonic fashion. One finds the source of generative form in dynamic human terms, such as gathering, or dispersal, or stop. Le Corbusier limits generative human qualities in urban architecture to "air," "green," and "sun," while exponents of group-form find a myriad of suggestive activities to add to that list of elements.

Addition of activities to physical qualities in a search for form determinants in the city suggests a new union between physical design and planning. We have long deplored the separation of architecture and planning. Perhaps the static, compositional methods of the past have been completely outmoded now by the rapid demands of a new technology and a new social organization. For thousands of years, architects have endeavored to build perfect buildings. The idea of a single structure, independent of other structures, has come from the Pyramids, the Parthenon, the Gothic cathedral, to the Seagram Tower, and the monumental building is an event, a pause, in the dynamic pattern of the city. One makes static compositions of individual buildings, and only subsequently can they become aspects of the grain of the city. The vital image of group-form, on the other hand, derives from a dynamic equilibrium of generative elements—not a composition of stylized and finished objects.

What is the vocabulary of collective form? We have spoken of a system of forms. Here are the components of those forms, as they differ from the traditional elements of single structures:

1. Wall: Any element which separates space horizontally. Walls are the place where forces outside and forces inside interact, and the manner of the interactions define the form and functions of the wall.

2. Floor: Any element which separates space vertically. In a broad sense, "floor" includes underground, ground and water surfaces, man-made floors, and even floating elements in the air. Basically roof gardens and green parks on the ground are only different in their levels, and not in their functions.

3. Shaft: Architecturally, it is a column, but environmentally it is an element which transfers men and their burdens from one level to another. A column is the element which transfers vertical loads, whereas in the collective form, the shaft transfers functions vertically.

4. Unit: A cell or block which performs a specific function. Here, architectural wall, floor, and roof are integrated to produce volumes and to represent a unit situation functionally.

5. Link: A link is the space which connects two or more spaces and objects. The spaces connected by a link may have diverse functions and quality. There are many kinds of link: physically connected link, implying link, built-in link, etc.

The above vocabulary of group-form and of collective form in general is not a set of definitions of form. It is a set of definitions of functional relations which may become a great many forms—the functional relation must precede formal thinking.

One may think of the functions in urban design as being patterns of human activities as they express the process of being alive in cities. The functional patterns are crystallized activities patterns.

The visual implications of such crystallized patterns of human activity become immediately apparent. The way in which one activity becomes another as groups of people move from travel, to work, to shipping, to dining, suggests the physical qualities which are commonly used to express transformation in physical design—rhythm, change, and contrast.

Characteristic spaces may be named in accord with the way in which human groups use them, i.e., transitional space, inward space, outward space, etc.

It is only in combining the environmental with the purely physical-visual aspects of form that investigations of group-form and urban form in general will be meaningful.

Tokyo, already the biggest city in the world, will add another 6 million people to its present 9 million by 1975. Greater Tokyo will eventually become a megalopolis of 25 million people. Shortages in shelters, public facilities, and green areas that this growth is likely to cause are appalling to contemplate. For example, although major thoroughfares are already half-paralyzed by the flow of automobiles, the city must expect the number of cars to multiply several times within a few years. In Tokyo, the amount of land being used for vehicular streets is less than 10 per cent of the whole, whereas the proportion in Western cities runs somewhere between 25 per cent and 35 per cent.

While the consensus is that more money should be invested both by government and by private business for the improvement of our city environs, the hard reality is that the Japanese economy today depends so much on the export of manufactured products that Japan cannot easily divert money from industry into public facilities, which requires far greater capital, and shows a much slower return than industry.

In the face of these almost insurmountable problems, two things in the field of planning seem to be urgently needed:

1. The establishment of a *proper master program* for the environmental structure of a future Tokyo.

2. The inauguration of dynamic *pilot projects* here and there within the framework of the master program.

These projects would form the cells and cores for future development. Despite considerable expenditure of manpower and money, existing public works are often criticized, and rightly so, for their inefficiency and lack of organization. The reason for failure of public works is the absence of a

goal, of a final objective in terms of which every project is oriented, executed, and evaluated. Never before has Tokyo had a master plan or a master program which would enhance the city's own broad prospects as well as those of Japan as a whole. The kind of plan needed would provide not only traffic and land use patterns, but concrete time-space schemes for complex modern living and for urban structures in which dynamic processes of modern society can evolve.

Never in their long history have the Japanese people ever built or lived in actual physical city-states of the European type. Tokyo is no exception. Due to frequent fires, earthquakes, and other calamities, today's Tokyo retains very few traces of the rich urban life it once contained, whereas European cities often have a physical charm which stems from the accumulation of buildings and streets preserved from generation to generation. In the modern period Tokyo has acquired sturdy concrete buildings which will last for years to come. Still the city lacks any significant community project which its residents can proudly regard as a symbol of modern Japan.

Tokyo is, however, a dynamo—the liveliness and color of city life exude from its millions of industrious people. We have all the building techniques and materials needed to insure the permanency of the city's physical structure. We have many young architects and planners, a reservoir of brains and enthusiasm sufficient to cope with complex large-scale projects. Even available money, though scarce and ineffectual when dispersed among many projects, would suffice if used properly. Tokyo is indeed one of the most highly industrialized political and economic centers in the world. There are not only possibilities for numerous ventures, but proportionate chances for success. That is why pilot projects become particularly significant here. This great urban complex offers an infinity of opportunities to manifest our dreams for a city of tomorrow.

The psychological effect of a pilot project, once realized, would doubtless be tremendous, for one concrete example is more persuasive than hundreds of paper schemes or thousands of words. How wonderful it would be if the chaotic, stifled downtown of Tokyo had a city plaza where people could sit and talk under the shade of trees; or if there were even one housing development in the city where each family could enjoy urban life with modern facilities, sunshine, trees, and quiet, and where children could play without danger from passing automobiles.

The following is a study which has been done with two purposes in mind: one is the investigation of various possible

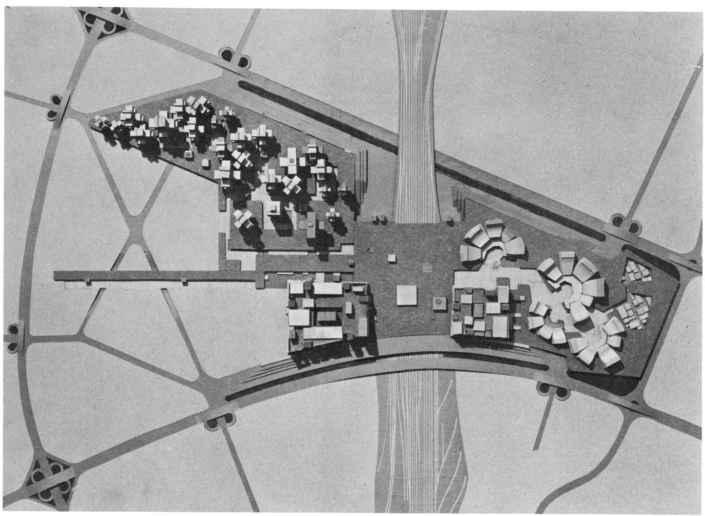

Shinjuku Redevelopment Project

collective forms; the other is the exploration of ideas which might be applicable for urban pilot projects in Japan.

Shinjuku is one of the biggest commercial and amusement subcenters of Tokyo. Every day over a million people use or pass the Shinjuku Terminal. The land value around the terminal is one of the highest in Tokyo, yet without intensive use proportional to the value. Most of the existing structures are either one or two stories, rarely more than three. Recently, however, more and more high rise office buildings are being built at the west side of the terminal.

This is a proposal to reorganize existing chaotic traffic situations around the terminal into a more orderly pattern and at the same time suggest new shopping, amusement, and office blocks under more intensive land use, thus relieving a certain amount of land for the recreation and high rise residential structures (Figs. 6–7).

The area taken for this proposal runs approximately one mile from west to east. Two major highways which connect downtown Tokyo with one of the most densely settled commuter zones are north and south boundaries.

The rail terminal is strategically located at the center of the area. Through multi-level platforms for rapid transit systems, subways, trains, buses, and automobiles, the flow of

people will be spread in four directions. Except for approaches to the terminal through underground tunnels, all automobiles will be parked at parking structures along the major highways, thus making the inside area completely free from vehicular traffic.

Master form: Shopping, amusement, and office blocks are expandable. The overall form is somewhat loose. We call this "master form." The master form is not a static composition, but is a state of equilibrium sustained by given elements. The concept of "master planning" has often been criticized for several reasons: first, the whole plan cannot be comprehended until it is completed; second, when completed it may well become socially obsolete or at least obsolescent. At worst, the plan is never completed. A master plan is basically a static concept, whereas the concept of master form we are proposing here is more elastic and capable of enduring despite changes in the society. Master form is one of the principles of a more dynamic approach in urban design.

In this project the concept of the *collective form* is applied as follows:

In the amusement squares, for instance, "gathering" is a main theme. The plaza forms a center about which opera houses, theaters, concert halls, movie theaters, variety theaters, etc. radiate like petals of a flower. Several plazas are linked together and form the amusement area. We think that this is a kind of form which retains the total image, even if individual elements were designed differently by several architects.

In the multi-level shopping centers which are directly accessible from the terminal, "milling" of people who engage in retailing, wholesaling, window-shopping, drinking, eating, chatting and passing, is the theme which determines the character of the space. It contains shops and stores of various styles and kinds—Western, Japanese, Chinese and Indian. Vertical service shafts are the only permanent elements in the structures. Floors will be extended freely vertically and horizontally; shop areas, access lanes, and passageways are also freely changeable, depending upon needs at a given time.

In the office town, a group of towers in various sizes and heights extends densely in a tight area like the Milky Way. Once, Le Corbusier said that "air" and "sun" are the basic needs for humane working place in urban environment. Today however we have air-conditioning systems and fluorescent light. Thus here, the vista and the development of interesting vistas from the windows of the buildings becomes the main consideration. The group of cantilever elements protruded from main shafts start to compose dynamic vistas. The roofs of the cantilevers become gardens.

Elements and systems have been developed through several themes which are generated from human association such as "gathering," "milling," and "vista." This is an attempt to create a total image through grouping of elements that is a reflection of growth and decay in our life process—a metabolic process. This is an attempt to conceive a form in relationship to an ever-changing whole and its parts. This is also an attempt to express the energy and sweat of millions of people in Tokyo, of the breath of life and the poetry of living.

Local Shopping District Development

Street patterns of Tokyo may well be described as labyrinthian. One can vaguely discern two major directions in the whole pattern of streets—one is radially projecting from the central district toward the outskirts, and the other is circumferential. The dense development of minor streets between them, however, tends to make the whole pattern a continuous web (Fig. 8).

Small shops, stores and restaurants, mostly one or two stories high and occasionally mingled with small factories, make continuous linear development along with the streets where street cars (artery) and bus systems run. Small residences attached to the rear of commercial structures are usually occupied either by those who own the shops or by

others in low income groups. These areas are easy prey for developing slum conditions. Surrounded by these areas, the inner areas usually consist of more decent residences, though the degree of decency generally depends on the specific topography and locality of the district.

The coexistence of streetcars, trucks, buses, automobiles, motorcycles, bicycles, pedestrians, and shopping activities in narrow streets presents a tremendous hazard both for traffic efficiency and for safety of pedestrians and children.

Our proposal is to develop shopping districts perpendicular to the streets so that shopping activity and traffic are separated (Figs. 9–10). This also helps to reorganize the undifferentiated urban façade by giving punctuation of greens, shops and residences. Two parallel walls (the inside of which can be used as either offices or storage space) make the basic skeleton of this shopping development. The area between the walls and the row of columns will be taken and furnished freely by individual retailers. The pedestrian walk can be raised half-level so that shops above and below will have same access from the walk. The top of the walks is covered by a roof as in many existing shopping districts in Japan.

After the prototype is established, many different forms and volumes can be developed according to given situations. One might have a cross plan, thus establishing a center for an open plaza; another might be a complex form growing from environmental complexity.

Fig. 8. Plan illustrating the typical layout of existing shopping districts in a Japanese city, which are arranged in a continuous linear development along the streets.

Fig. 9. Plan illustrating the proposal of Maki and Ohtaka for the development of shopping districts in Japanese cities, which would be arranged perpendicular to the streets.

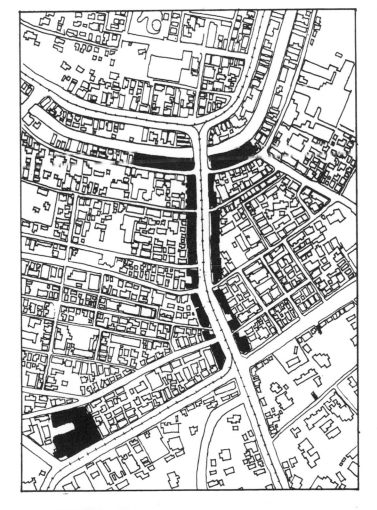

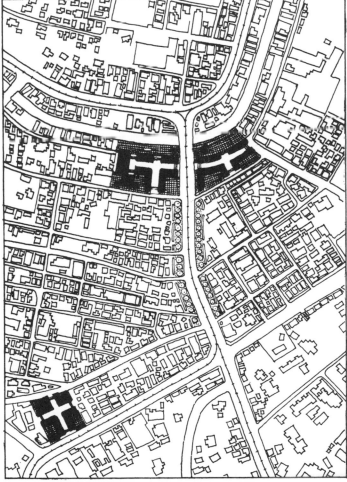

Fig. 10. Maki and Ohtaka. Model of Prototype Shopping District.
(Photo Watanabe)

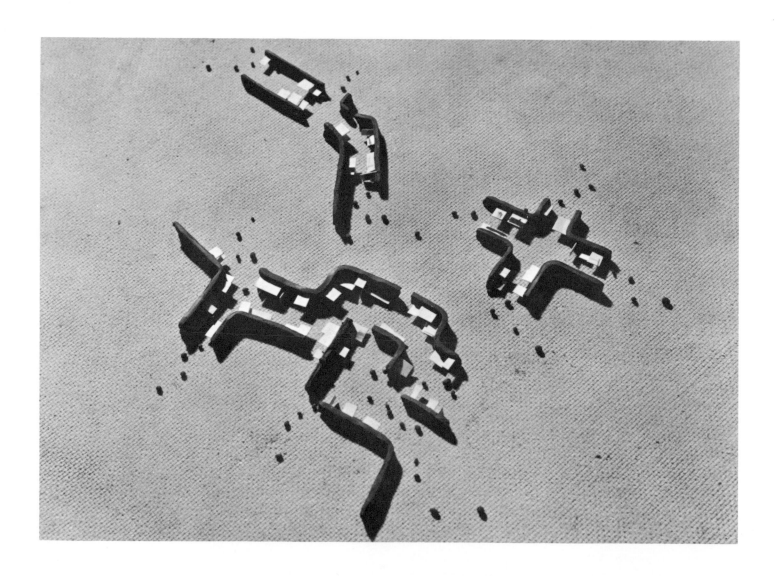

Regionalism and Collective Form

In the age of mass communication and technological facility, regional differences throughout the world are becoming less well-defined. Though we are here primarily concerned with this fact as it relates to the form of the city, it is apparent that in general it is becoming less easy to find distinctive expressions of cultural difference in human activities.

If materials and methods of construction are becoming ubiquitous in this world, perhaps their combination, especially in large complexes of form, will remain a distinguishing characteristic of the place in which they are used and the persons who use them. Thus it may be possible to find regionalism within the urban scale, but very little in single buildings. The primary locus of regional character in urban landscape will possibly be in the grain of the city.

Two thoughts on the possible relations between regional characteristics and modern technology exist.

The first and dominant one is that regional differences and regional characteristics in human environment are rapidly disappearing under the impact of modern technology; and that eventually the differences could be diminished to a point where every region will be dominated by a single set of living and behavior patterns and a common environmental framework.

The second is diametrically opposed to the first. Homogeneization of environment is not the inevitable result of technology. Technology can produce entirely new products, but with modern communication systems those new products will soon be transmitted to other regions, thus becoming no longer characteristic regional products. This process will continue and intensify with time. Entirely new regional products will be born and will be assimilated or disappear. But assimilation of extra-regional products does not imply disappearance of the regional characteristics which differentiate areas.

This observation leads to a new definition of "regionalism." Regionalism does not arise from characteristic indigenous elements or products, but rather from the manner in which such generalized elements are evaluated, organized and expressed. In other words, *regionalism is an expression of a character form of association of elements* (products), rather than a direct expression of singular elements. We call this *open regionalism*. [4] The open regionalism is a dynamic process itself, sustained by the tension created by two poles within the society.

The development of town planning and urban design has reached the point where the quest for regionalism on this level becomes vitally important. And group-form and megaform affect the urban milieu at precisely that level. They are methods of clustering small scale elements. In both megaform and group-form, the possibility for creating grain elements, hence regional qualities, exists. In megaform, the frame is a large enough single element to be significant as grain. It is a large form, which represents all the power of technique and which may represent the best aspects of regional selectivity. In group-form the generative element itself may reflect regional quality. The reciprocal relation between the generative element and its system can produce strongly regional effects, evolving from a unique social pattern and its particular value system.

Summary

These three approaches to collective form which have been discussed here—compositional form, megastructure and group-form—are not plans; they are models of thinking about the possible ways to deal with rather large complex urban design. It is most likely that in any final form of architecture or plan, these three concepts will appear either combined or mixed.

This paper was meant to be somewhat polemic, to stimulate further discussion. One thing, however, is clear and important: that is, the need for a new concept and study of collective form. The collective form has its own unique properties which are absent or latent in single buildings. Further investigation in this direction would contribute not only to the art of making large-scale forms but also to the designing of individual buildings.

1. The idea of sequential development has recently been discussed by Roger Montgomery, who sees the series of buildings or elements without apparent beginning or end as a contemporary "theme" of composition, distinct from the closed forms which characterized classic or axial "themes" of composition.
2. Kenzo Tange discusses this idea at length in a series of three articles in *Japan Architect* (October, 1960).
3. John Voelker, in his CIAM Team X report in *Carré Blue* discusses this idea of an open aesthetics in referring to work of Hansen and Soltan in Poland.
4. The idea of "open regionalism" was initially conceived by Roger Montgomery and Fumihiko Maki at Washington University.

This pair of fundamentals, this key and lock combination, will here be discussed chiefly in terms of verbal structure and verbal communication. I know more about these than about, for example, the structure of the visual and visual communications or the structure of music and communication through that. But I will venture to predict that anyone who is knowledgeable in painting or in music will, if he explores the following pages, find himself easily able to note any number of analogies in his own field. What is analogy but some degree of identity in difference as to structure?

The dependence of communication on structure is, of course, a field of studies that has at many points advanced incredibly in the last forty years: the statistical theory of communication and the physics which enable us to exchange messages with satellites and to steer missiles, for example. Nothing in these triumphs has made the deficiencies in communication I am concerned with any the less alarming. Nothing of all that we can now do in physics makes misunderstanding less dangerous or lessens the need to do what we can about it. I shall be arguing that there is much that we can and should do and that present obstacles to our doing it could be quickly overcome if we would realize how immediate the need is.

There have been other advances—equally astonishing—in our knowledge, for example, of the communication media used by bees and ants, and by other organisms which may inherit the earth if we can't mend our ways in time. Still more unexpected is our dawning knowledge of how cells tell their successors how to behave and of the code operations that direct heredity. All this again does not make our ever-mounting capacity to meddle with the genes any less threatening.

It is against such a background of urgencies that I want to ask whether the study of language may not call for rather a different selection of emphases than has been customary in recent years. Linguistic advances have been chiefly in technical resources for *describing* languages. So much progress here has been achieved that it is perhaps inevitable that most linguistic specialists should regard continuance of this descriptive effort as the chief, if not the only task to pursue. They are loth to listen to those who suggest that descriptive linguistics has for some time been well enough developed to allow revolutionary work to be done on the design of language learning. It has been customary to say, for example, that we need to know more about the structure of English before we can really study how it may best be taught. This looks plausible, perhaps, until we consider how very far apart the linguists' conceptual accounts still are from the actualities that are operative in the most successful learning of language. The most successful learner is a child to whom any linguistic account of what he is learning or of what he is doing as he learns is quite unintelligible. And yet, in a sense, it *is* the child's business as he learns to understand his task—but not in terms of any linguistic account of it. The job of making the task intelligible to the child—or to any less apt learner—belongs to the designer of instruction not to the linguistician. The designer of instruction will use, of course, all he can learn of linguistics, as of other neighboring subjects, but essentially his study will be guided by the outcomes of his experiments. In brief, design of instruction is a self-governing field of study.

What I will attempt here is to sketch some sort of overall picture of it in terms of which we can frame a synoptic plan of priorities—or at least ask some questions toward this.

This sketch, plan, synopsis, calls for a series of diagrams. It is remarkable, I shall be suggesting, how much we neglect in our discussions the aid which practice with diagrams could render. Of our two major channels, the eye is comprehensive and relational, the ear serial and discursive. In due combination the powers of both are increased.

My first diagram is the traditional series of boxes which the communications engineer finds convenient:

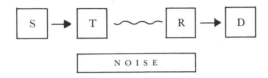

Having that, through the pictorial channel, compactly present to you, I can proceed, through the verbal channel, to discuss it. S is a Source of Messages from which any Message can be selected and handed to a Transmitter, T, which converts it into a Signal (the wavy line), which reaches a Receiver, R, which hands it to D, a Destination. The remaining box represents NOISE: characters of the signal not correspondent with the Message as selected from the Source, additions, distractions, fade outs . . . that sort of thing. Note, though, how easily we misdescribe: "things are added to the signal which were not intended by the information source" (C. E. Shannon and W. Weaver, *The Mathematical Theory of Communication*, 1949, p. 99). Words like "intended" do not properly belong here. As we shall see, there can be great and dangerous confusion over this.

Contrast now another representation:

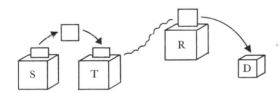

Source: a file. Anything whatever may be on the sheets which pass from the file to the transmitter. The communications engineer (as engineer) is utterly indifferent to the character of the Message. All he is concerned with is to get the Message correctly reproduced on the sheet which issues from the Receiver—on the Moon, say. The Messages may be utter nonsense. He doesn't mind, provided that what goes into Transmitter can be compared with what comes out from Receiver and be checked as correct or incorrect. What any message says is as irrelevant as those varying expressions on the face of the Message I have chosen to put in. In brief, the engineer (as engineer) is concerned only with the physical.

Contrast now:

As a visual communication proceeding somehow from me (as we say) to you (as we say) this is, I hope you'll agree, rather different from that sheet which came out of the file into the Transmitter, was reproduced in the Receiver and went on into the wastepaper basket. We are concerned here with Meaning and with Interpretation—the most inexhaustible subjects for discussion that can be found. To be true to its own conditions my diagram can do no more than invite you to try your own hand with this warning question: How often can what follows R coincide with what preceded T?

The three points I would like this diagram to make are these: 1) Source and Destination are open-ended. The whole process or transaction is deeply concerned with WHENCE and WHITHER, with what has gone into the forming of the message and with what is to ensue from its re-embodiment in you. 2) At a certain stage (namely when my pencil puts down its film of graphite on the paper to be photographed by the block-maker, to be impressed on the page, to be reproduced on your retinas) the message *died*. It became, as we say, *merely physical*. And then as you began to "see" it (in various senses of "see"); began to compare it with diagrams one and two: began to wonder why S and D are open-ended; to wonder what the boxes between S and T and between R and D represent and what their relations could suggest . . . as all this went on (I hope it did or will) the message began to come to life again, to be re-embodied (with differences, of course) in you—after its passage through the lifeless signal and the merely mechanical processes of being prepared for transmission and of optical reception. In this re-embodiment my words—accompaniments to your visual apprehension—will have joined. 3) Your interpretation of the message as a whole (or of any feature of it) depends upon its relations to other messages, past and present. It means whatever it can mean to anyone through connections with other messages and especially through contrasts with other things which it does *not* mean.

In brief, utterance and interpretation are *selective* in a sense in which physical transactions are not.

I have been trying to suggest some major differences between the problems the communications engineer handles so brilliantly—with such frightening brilliance—and those with which the psychologist muddles about so confusedly. I have been hoping to remind you that the physicist succeeds because he can ignore so much. What Whitehead used to call "essential neglect" enables him to set himself relatively far simpler tasks. The student of meaning can not do that. One of his worst difficulties, in fact, is that he is always so strongly tempted to try to do it, to try, by drastic simplifications, to get himself a more manageable undertaking. In recent decades the most famous of these attempts has been Behaviorism. In spite of all that has been learned from the endeavours of Behaviorists, it may be suggested that what Behaviorism has chiefly demonstrated—through these 40 years—is its insufficiency. To substitute Behavior for Meaning has been to miss the point—the point at which really vital progress can be and must be made. I am reminded of Oppenheimer's fine cry: "It is the business of science to be wrong!" Behaviorism has discovered a great deal in detail about behavior but in general has it not shown just this: that the key problems are beyond it?

It will make this a little solider, perhaps, if I juxtapose now two pronouncements: one from B. F. Skinner, the other from Noam Chomsky's review of Skinner's book, *Verbal Behavior*.

Here is Skinner: "Hundreds of puzzling questions and obscure propositions about verbal behavior may be dismissed while the new questions and propositions which arise to take their place are susceptible to experimental check as part of a more unified pattern." [B. F. Skinner, *Verbal Behavior* (1957) p. 456.]

Here is Chomsky on that: "The questions to which Skinner has addressed his speculations are hopelessly premature. It is futile to enquire into the causation of verbal behavior until much more is known about the specific character of this behavior; and there is little point in speculating about the process of acquisition without much better understanding of what is acquired." [Noam Chomsky, in *Language* (Jan.-Mar. 1959) p. 55.]

What may strike us first is the extreme confidence of both pronouncements. How, for example, does Skinner know what these questions and propositions are that are being "dismissed" if they are so puzzling and obscure? And in what sense do the new questions and propositions "take their place"? Do they attempt the same tasks, for example? To change the subject is often a way of dodging an inquiry.

The Chomsky comment, as the sentences I quote read, might still be Behaviorism—it is only in the actual procedures he hopes may lead us towards "better understanding" that the differences appear. Chomsky is a consortium of modern descriptive linguistics, modern logic and modern methodology —encouraging one another in the pursuit of rigor. But if we ask rather relentlessly about this rigor and what it depends upon, we get a very interesting answer. It depends upon mental procedures about which as yet almost nothing whatever is known, upon innumerable "acts of immediate perception", acts of intellectual vision about which we can as yet say little more than that they are complex and various comparisons of structure and that all the rest of our mental procedure turns on them.

Look, for example, at these two sentences of Chomsky's. We can *see* innumerable things about them: we can *see* which words they are composed of and how these words cooperate. We can *see* that the second sentence is explaining and justifying what the first has said. Of any one word or phrase in either of them we can *see* that some substitutions of other words are possible (in various ways) and that other substitutions are not possible . . . and so on indefinitely. Well! How do we *see* any or all of these things? What sorts of *seeings* are these? How different they are. Compare 1) seeing that *It* and *is* are different words, 2) seeing that *It* must come before *is* in this sentence, 3) seeing that *speculations* is related to *speculating*, 4) seeing that there is a big and peculiar sniff or snort at Skinner in the use of either word: *speculations* (ha!) *speculating* (hum!). All these "seeings" are different; all are highly complex. They are hierarchic—some depend upon others. We must *see* which word a word is before we can *see* how it interacts with others, and we must have *seen* how it so interacts before we can *see* that *speculations*, for example, is pejorative in its use here.

On such matters competent users of a language achieve remarkable agreement. I am not inviting anyone to doubt that. Indeed it is my main point. All use of language—all agreement or disagreement on further matters that can be brought about through language—depends upon competence in such immediate perceptions of facts of linguistic structure.

Pause for a moment to consider how queer it is that theorists in these matters still, in general, pay so little attention to these linguistic perceptions which are prerequisites to all their further operations. It is as though a student of physical vision were to say: "Don't let's bother about the eye and how it works and all that! What we care about is WHAT we see, not HOW." There is, I suggest, an analogous neglect in the study of communication. We are so busy with WHAT we may have to say that we continually neglect vital considerations about the HOW of all saying and of all comprehension of what may be being said. We do well to ponder the metaphor of intellectual vision as fully and as carefully as we can.

IMMEDIATE PERCEPTION	INTERPRETATION
HOW?	WHAT?
LINGUISTIC VISION	THINGS SAID
◁)	⊄]
PHYSICAL VISION	THINGS SEEN

I come now to our most urgent needs in the study of communication. The chief need is to improve our performance in these immediate perceptions of how words work together, these immediate perceptions upon which all saying and all comprehension of what may be being said depend. We will have to improve performance (and quickly and at all levels from the bottom up and from the top down) or else.

Why is this becoming increasingly urgent?

For an obvious and inescapable reason. Technological advances everywhere—and not least in the physical achievements of the communications engineer—force upon us an ever-mounting, planet-wide need for talent, for ability. Talent is always the world's worst shortage. There are never enough able enough people to go round. And with every wave of innovation this shortage gets worse. There is only one possible remedy. A great and swift improvement in our techniques for producing ability in people. In other words, advances in the technology of education commensurate with the need. To be specific, this comes down to rapid development of DESIGN in sequenced (programmed) instruction through film, tape and "teaching machine"—and in the use of the major media: Radio, Text and TV, through which such programmed, or better, sequenced instruction can be disseminated.

DESIGN here is the key word: *design* in organizing the cooperations of eye and ear in presentation, design in the *serial ordering* of acts of perception; design in bringing together mutually helpful patterns of relationship.

The essential principle of all such design is that *what comes first should prepare for what follows and what follows should strengthen and clarify what has come before.* This is, of course, one of the oldest truisms of pedagogy. It comes to life, though, in an entirely new fashion when we can control, through film and tape, the minutest particulars of presentation, when we can stabilize experimental arrangements, and when we can collect reliable data as to the performances of students with them. These possibilities of control, I repeat, are new. Now for the first time we can really come near to knowing what we are doing to the student and what he is doing with what we offer him. With a modern sequenced teaching film or with a well sequenced string of problems posed through a teaching machine, the student learns through USING what he knows already on a new and manageable task which is just sufficiently novel. His work is an exercise and development of his acquired powers in a series of acts of perception of the new. The design of such sequenced presentation is by no means an easy matter. It has to be learned by the designer, who learns through his mistakes—to which he is forced to pay proper attention. I go back to Oppenheimer's cry: "It is the business of science to be wrong." Fortunately, in modern design of instruction, every passage of attempted teaching through film presentation or through machine administered course can be a lesson to the instructor—in how to arrange things better for the learner, in how to bring out in the learner the kinds of abilities he and the world most need.

"The kinds of ability the world most needs"—what are these? First and foremost, ability to *inquire*, ability to *compare*, ability to *select on the basis of comparing*, ability to *try out*, ability *to see what the outcome* of the trial is, *ability to change one's mind* through seeing how and why the view taken has been wrong. In brief, *intelligent exploratory conduct*.

Being able to read or to speak a second language—these are assets; but having *learned how to learn*—through these acquisitions—is a far greater asset. Any design in instruction must be judged in terms of the improvement in *learning capacity* it induces. But we must see "learning capacity" here in terms of the activities I have just mentioned: inquiring, comparing, selecting, trying views out, observing outcomes and inquiring again. It is these abilities rather than the mere reproduction of received impressions that we most need to cultivate. Of course, retention comes into them all. What we have done always guides what we will do. All intelligent exploratory conduct selectively applies what it has learned already in going on to learn more.

Let me take a few examples. I will take them from the earliest stages of learning a second language and of learning to read—so sequenced as to induce as much *learning how to learn* as possible. These two: early second language work and reading, are the fields in which the new techniques of sequencing have been most fully experimented with and themselves explored.

The unit in language learning is *a sentence in a situation*. Let me depict this so:

$$\begin{matrix} \text{A Sentence} \\ \text{in} \\ \text{A Situation} \end{matrix} \quad : \quad \frac{\text{S E N}}{\text{S I T}}$$

The depiction, I hope, suggests that the SITUATION encloses the SENTENCE. The situation *in* which it is used gives meaning to the sentence.

$$\text{i.e.} \quad \frac{\text{S E N}}{\text{S I T}}$$

Such a formulation needs refining, of course. We need to distinguish individual instances of sentences: sen-a^1, sen-a^2 . . . and situations: sit-a^1, sit-a^2 . . . from the more or less conventional standard forms under which we may sort them. Sen-a^1, sen-a^2 . . . may all differ in many respects without ceasing to be examples of SEN-A. So may sit-a^1, sit-a^2 . . . vary and yet be cases of SIT-A. All our thinking: our sorting, discriminating, connecting activities, all our *intelligent exploratory conduct* in the sense described above is woven of comparings of SEN and SIT's. We can, of course, generalize SEN to cover any mode of representation or notation as we can generalize SIT to cover whatever may in any fashion be represented: treated through a notation.

In the beginnings of learning a second language we should use contrasts between SEN/SIT's such that the sentences and the situations which give them meaning vary observably together. In other words we should use *contrastive procedure*. What the learner should be trying to do is to see how the language works. What we, as teachers, should be trying to do is to arrange sequences which will make this as easy as possible for him.

The phrase "contrastive procedure" may invite a misunderstanding. The contrasts that should be used are contrasts *within the new language,* not contrasts *between it and the mother tongue.* They are *intra*-lingual contrasts, not *inter*-lingual contrasts. The mother tongue should be (as far as possible and this can be very far) *cut out* in new language learning. The method should be direct, but it must be a controlled and graded direct method—which is to say that its precise sequencing is all-important. There has been much misunderstanding on all this. Many linguists have supposed that int*er*-lingual studies must be the key to language teaching. They were confusing what can be achieved in a Graduate School with what can happen in the infant school and can be made possible in general.

In good int*ra*-lingual contrastive procedure the SEN/SIT's offered for comparison should be arranged to invite and guide attention to *what varies with what.* Here is where the combination of film presentation, pictured text and programming through teaching machine comes in. To notice what varies with what is, of course, the root of scientific method.

In beginning a new language the contrasts which should invite this attention to co-variants are, broadly speaking, of three kinds: 1) between sentences as saying this or that; 2) between words as working together in this way or that; 3) between sounds as making this word different from that. It is important that the learner should take these three sorts of contrasts together *from the first.* He has to take them together in all field *use* of the language. There is no reason why his study of the language should not use this growing knowledge from the first: use it to extend it—as we all do with our native language all our lives.

There need be little or no *drill* in language learning. *Drill* may rhyme with *skill* but it also rhymes with *kill*. When we are *using* language, what we are doing is essentially *choosing*. *To use* rhymes with *to choose*.

Learning how to compare and select, to see what goes along with or changes with what: nothing is better than beginning language study for developing that. In fact it was through doing that with our first language that we became human. Here is a current account of the process: "The child who learns a language has in some sense constructed the grammar for himself on the basis of his observation of sentences and nonsentences. . . . Furthermore, this task is accomplished in an astonishingly short time, to a large extent independently of intelligence, and in a comparable way by all children. Any theory of learning must cope with these facts." [Noam Chomsky, in *Language* (Jan.-Mar., 1959) p. 57.] The strange thing is that experimental studies of early stages of second language learning, finding out what facilitates and what frustrates, have been so slow to develop.

Turn now to learning to read and write (or should we say write and read?)—learning, that is, how to use a notation for speech. Notations are enormously important things—the history of any subject, from mathematics on down, or on up if you please, is largely a history of the development of its notations. Linguistics itself is a fine example. Learning to read, learning how to use our first notation, is a terrific opportunity to learn how to learn. *Terrific,* indeed! Mess and muddle here can entail mess and muddle in all our later intellectual enterprises. Worse still, it can, *and does,* preclude, in many cases, other intellectual enterprises. The non-literate can sometimes be an immensely effective person. The frustrated person who has tried his best and failed to learn to read, or has succeeded (if we should call it that) at the cost of permanent aversion to mental work, is our greatest current social problem.

Aversion: Here is where I would like to pay my tribute to B. F. Skinner, that bold pioneer in so many fields, who has best pointed out how dangerous and unnecessary fear is as a motive in learning. Fear, as we all know, tends to spread. If we have cause to fear failure in a task, we come to fear the challenge itself. The right motive in learning is the intrinsic reward of increased power. A proper arrangement of early steps into reading must offer the fascination of successful exploration from the start. It must guide the attention again and again to the points at which rewarding discoveries can occur.

Suppose we begin instruction in Reading with sentences using only a set of seven letters, letters as distinct, one from another, as possible. Suppose we write sentences with them which correspond to situations which can be simply and *undistractingly* depicted.

This is a man

This is a hat

———————————

a hi mn st

How can the points of contrast at which the sentence varies with the situation be made maximally apparent? Cut out, at this stage, all other variables. Keep the syntax uniform, keep to the third person of the naming and descriptive statement, keep out the dramatic incalculables of first and second persons. Similarly in the depictions keep out whatever is likely to be distracting. Then you will have conditions which are on the way, at least, toward making the learner's task of seeing how the notation works as easy for him as it can be.

The first comment of those used to current conventional practice will be: "How dull! What is there here to interest the learner?" In actual fact the simplicity and obviousness of the immediate perceptions to which the design invites the learner make the following of their interconnections a fascinating exploration. The lure of the task itself and the intrinsic rewards of success in it: these are the proper inducement—not any adventitious jollying-up.

The deliberate, planned avoidance of *distraction* is one of the points about this procedure which strikes those coming newly to it as strange. The efforts of most beginning texts to seem exciting, vivid, colorful to the learner are all in the opposite direction. My old friend and collaborator, C. K. Ogden,— in *The Meaning of Meaning* days, forty years back—took A. N. Whitehead's celebrated Method of *Extensive Abstraction* and invented an opposite, a Method of *Intensive Distraction.*

*Ex*tensive *Ab*straction

*In*tensive *Dis*traction

This looks like an exercise in Reading, doesn't it? Actually, it displays a contrast which is a key to all design in the sequencing of instruction. What we have to do is to give the learner the best chance possible to ABSTRACT from the sequences of materials put before him the *structure* on which its modes of working depend. And to *abstract* this structure as extensively as possible, up and down through all the linguistic levels: meaning, form, sound; sound, form, meaning.

Learning to read is not (as some have supposed) simply learning how letters and sounds *(writtens and spokens)* correspond *or don't*. It is very much more than this:

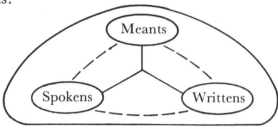

It is studying over again—with the new aid that the written notation provides—how language works—through the inter-linkage at all levels of samenesses and differences in linguistic structure: an inquiry that in no one should really ever end. And that is why learning to read is such an opportunity, such a second chance to learn to think.

If we could just stop bungling this second entry into the abilities that our too-accelerated world most needs, we would have taken an immense step forward. Constructive, forward-looking, and responsible sequencing is hardest to design near the beginning of any subject. And there, near the beginning, what you do and don't do matters most. It is there that the cognitive patterns, or sets, are formed. Later on in the subject you have indefinitely more choices open and just what you do next makes less and less difference; we have less to learn there about learning.

I am hoping that this brief sketch of the dependence of communication—in the instance of verbal language—upon direct apprehension of structure may sufficiently suggest its analogues with other modes of utterance: with teaching people to see better, for example. The problems of "visual illiteracy" are not minor. What proportion of people anywhere have really learned how to see? How many have learned how to hear?

Let me close, however, on an optimistic note. The promises that better sequencing holds out are not limited to language learning. That a new language can be taught *from zero on up* by sequenced film presentation and film directed exercise—taught on any scale you please to imagine—is established. If you can teach a new language so, you can teach anything through it. I might better say "along with it." While you are teaching a language why not teach the most important things it can handle as well? Teach them not as formulae to be recited, but as topics inviting exploration. This can be and is beginning to be done by film. It is a bad mistake to think that we should first teach a language; and *then* teach subject matters, attitudes to life, aspirations, morals, positions for living, through it. We do much better by realizing, right from the start, that what makes a language worth learning is the things that it can help us to understand and to do. In our current world crisis of the coming in everywhere of the developing countries, their *coming together* rather into the fraternity of the peoples, the first priority, the prerequisite, is ways of learning to use the languages they need, ways which will really help us all to see better how to understand what to do.

SYNTACTIC STRUCTURE IN THE VISUAL ARTS

In the correspondence between André Gide and Paul Valéry, a letter can be found, where Valéry explains his "method": the attempt toward a systematic handling of language. It is a document dated 1899, thus from the period, when poets and painters, art as well as science, were striving for the same outcome: a new objectivity of the human communications. Valéry's letter is quoted at the beginning of this study, as it seems symptomatic for the situation toward the turn of the century; it is one of the documents that open a wide horizon on the varying approaches of the problem in twentieth century art. It is dated 16 October, 1899: "The very roots of 'mis-comprehension' are a part of the principal tendency of my spirit, which is that of extension and perpetual generalization. It is completely impossible for me to stick to any particular, unique thing. I can today give you a precise notion of this. All determined subjects for me reduce themselves to a series of physical and mental operations within certain limits. These limits are invariable; they are also as thought-out as possible. Now, these operations, above all the mental ones, can be acquired. The sole difficulty is to analyze well the given subject in order to reduce it for all possible cases to a group of positively dead elements, and to a scheme within a series of more or less spiritual actions. Finally, the mental operations are certainly of a finite and small number. This system which I have barely sketched out for you already completely covers many things, and even without my detailing its processes and requirements, you will have grasped its scope. One of the greatest advantages of this system is that it restricts to a minimum the possibility of muddling due to the language, for it does not take any account of the words but rather replaces them with their relational significance."[1]

Here we find the attempt to form a synthetic language, a language, that is, where not the words, but their context and their relations are of the utmost importance. This is a trend that dominates one of the currents of the visual arts from the beginning of our century unto the present day. It is prefigured in Valéry's letter, but it goes back even further, to the romantic theories of art in the beginning of the nineteenth century, to the attempt to find and to constitute a "basso generale" of the visual arts. In French art criticism, Baudelaire has set the key by writing: "nature is only a dictionary,"[2] implying by these lines that it is the artist's task to constitute a creation—a poem—out of these words which the dictionary of nature can furnish. And in his well-known sonnet "*Correspondences*" he stresses the relations of the different sensorial perceptions: "*les parfums, les couleurs et les sons se répondent,*" in terms of a language.

Nature is only a dictionary—but language, going far beyond the words listed there, is the human communication par excellence, and it is the artist's task and privilege to create and to renew the language. What makes language differ from the words in the dictionary is syntax, is the series of "mental operations" to quote from Valéry. He is a link in a long chain of artists, all of whom have thought about this aspect of communication: half a century before him Gustave Flaubert wrote: "Beauty will perhaps become a useless sentiment to humanity and art will be something which occupies the realm between algebra and music."[3]

In all these quotations the tendency is quite evident to constitute a syntactic system for the arts, a grammar, or as it is called by preference, a "basso generale." The musical language is preferred as an example, and from this analogy springs the priority of structural features on figurative elements, that is to say the tendency toward abstraction.

It is Seurat who was most preoccupied with this idea of a visual syntax. Though he did not elim-

Fig. 1. Georges Seurat. *The Café Singer*, 1887.

inate the figurative element in his paintings, he stressed the importance of composition, of the "mental operations." The concept of aesthetics that he has formulated shows clearly how he gives priority to syntax above the importance of the "words" (Fig. 1), which he finds in nature's dictionary: "Art is harmony. Harmony is the analogy of opposites, the analogy of similars, of tone, of color, of line considered by the dominant and under the influence of a lighting made up of combinations of gaiety, calmness and sadness. The opposites are: for tone, a tone more bright and light for one more dark; for color, the opposites are the complementaries, that is red opposed to its complementary, etc. (red-green; orange-blue; yellow-purple); for line, those forming a right angle. The gaiety of tone is where the dominant tone is bright; the gaiety of color where the dominant color is warm; and the gaiety of line, those lines which are upwardly directed. Calmness of tone is produced when the dark and light are equal; of color where the warm and cold are equal; and calmness of line is the horizontal. Sadness of tone is the dominance of dark; of color the dominance of cold; of line, those lines which are downwardly directed."[4]

This tendency toward abstraction, toward the syntactic values in the visual language, was further emphasized and enhanced at the same time by another figurative painter, Maurice Denis; in 1890 he wrote: "One should remember that a painting—before being a war-horse, a nude woman or some anecdote—is essentially a flat surface covered with colors arranged in a certain order."[5] In these words "arranged in a certain order" lies the syntactic value of his phrase: he stresses the importance, the autonomy, of the compositional order, quite apart from the necessity of figurative representation. He even gives priority to these compositional values: "before being a war-horse etc."

It is an essential fact here that all syntactic values, the components of language, to which Seurat, Denis and many others refer, belong to the domain of the flat plane, the strictly two-dimensional surface. It is on this surface that the language of painting is to be considered at home, and all the other values—of space, of reference to objects, of volume, of light and shade, etc.—enter into the scene only at a later moment. The flat surface—"a flat surface covered with colors arranged in a certain order"—is the primary condition of painting—or becomes so in the years around the turn of the century. Once the artist became conscious of the fact that he was speaking a language of his own, the conditions of this language began to be a problem, and the artist, in his unrelenting search for essential truth, and confronted by a changed and unexpected situation, began to face the facts of this problem.

How then did the artist—the painter—become conscious of the fact, that he was speaking—or that he was to speak—a language of his own? The problem can be traced back again to Baudelaire, who acquired his ideas and his criticism on the visual arts from Delacroix: the source of this concept springs, thus, from the romantic movement, from the concept of reality and the standards it was applying to painting and the other arts. In one of his essays, which constitute his *Art Romantique*, Baudelaire writes: "Now, what is a poet (I use the word in its broadest sense) if not a translator, a decoder?"[6] The words in parentheses permit us to apply this visionary statement not only to literary poetry, but to the visual arts as well.

Baudelaire himself has certainly meant it this way, as becomes clear from his many statements—mostly about Delacroix—where he uses the words "poetry" and "poet" for the art of a painter. And what else is a "translator"—an interpreter—than a man translating communications into a language of his own, on behalf of others receptive to the understanding of this language? The art and the skill of this interpreter therefore demands, first of all, a mastery of the language: not only the knowledge of the words, but the faculty to put words together into phrases, sentences—poems, in the broadest sense of the word. "Since I consider the impression transmitted to the artist as the most important thing to translate, is it not necessary that he be armed in advance with all the means for the most rapid translation?"[7] Here Baudelaire quotes Delacroix, and elsewhere he refers to another description of the same problem, that he had noted down "almost from the dictation of the master": "Nature is only a dictionary, he used to repeat frequently. In order to really understand the meaning of the implied sense of this phrase, it is necessary to consider the ordinary and numerous uses of the dictionary. One searches there the meaning of words, the generation of words, the etymology of words, and finally one takes from the dictionary all the elements which make up a phrase or a narration; but no one has ever considered the dictionary a composition in the poetic sense of the word."[8]

To this definition in the negative, Baudelaire adds a very clear positive statement in the course of the same essay: "Exterior nature only furnishes the artist with an endlessly recurring occasion to cultivate this germ; she is only an incoherent accumulation of material that the artist is invited to associate and to put in order, an incitement, a rouser to his sleeping faculties. Precisely speaking there is in nature neither line nor color. It is man who creates line and color. These are two abstractions which draw their equal nobility from the same origin."[9]

Line and color are human abstractions, they are the elementary means of the language of painting, and they presuppose the flat surface (the "flat surface" of Maurice Denis) as their category of existence. Stressing their importance—as Baudelaire has done—means giving priority to the structural entities of painting above the representational aspects, which a tradition of several centuries had raised to supreme honors. Where are the reasons for such a change in appreciation, for this new consciousness of the artist's means and tasks?

Baudelaire hints at one of the reasons, when opposing the art of painting to its counterpart (or even, in his period, its counterfeit), photography. He is the first lucid spirit in the nineteenth century to have unveiled the "industrial revolution" of the visual arts, even before the results of this revolution became visible: "In these deplorable days, a new industry has appeared, which is a fraud and contributes not a little to ruin that which might remain sacred in the French spirit. This idolatrous mass certainly preaches an ideal fitting and appropriate to its nature. In matters of painting and sculpture, the credo of these people, above all in France (I do not believe that anyone dare affirm the contrary) is this: 'I believe in nature and I believe in nature only. . . . I believe that art is and can be only the exact reproduction of nature. . . . Thus the industry which gives us a result which is identical to nature would be the absolute art.' A vengeful God fulfilled the vows of this multitude. Daguerre was its Messiah. And then they said to themselves: 'Since photography gives us all the guaranties of exactitude' (they believe that, in their stupidity) 'art is photography.' From this moment on, this vile society, like one great Narcissus, in order to contemplate its trivial image on metal, went head over heels. . . . Since the photographic industry was the refuge of all those unsuccessful painters, too little gifted, or too lazy to complete their studies, this universal infatuation carried with it not only blindness and imbecility, but also a sort of vengeance. That such a stupid conspiracy, in which as always one finds some evil persons and some dupes, could succeed in an absolute manner, I cannot believe, or at least I do not want to believe;

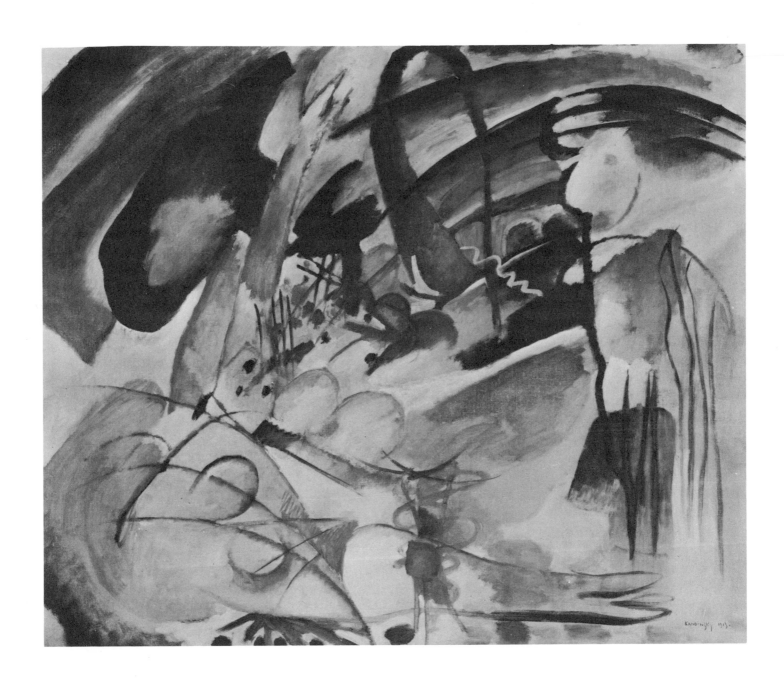

Fig. 2. Wassily Kandinsky. *Improvisation 33*, 1913.

Fig. 3. Piet Mondrian. *Composition*, 1922.

but I am convinced that the progress of photography badly applied has very much contributed, as all purely material progress, to the impoverishment of the French artistic genius, already so rare."[10]

The sharp and prophetic vision of Cassandra, conjured up by Baudelaire, has not come true. On the contrary, the innovation of photography has acted as a challenge, as a stimulus to the visual arts, obliging them to an "examen de conscience," to an analysis of their aims and means. Instead of stressing—as Baudelaire feared—the representational faculties of painting ("I believe that art is and can be only the exact reproduction of nature"), the eminent artists of the close of the nineteenth century turned to the structural possibilities, which the language of the arts came to disclose. Cézanne's statement that "art is a harmony parallel to nature" has to be understood in this light, and his idea that painting was "to think with the eyes" points in the same direction: nature—and this word also can now be used in its broadest significance—is to be translated into the language of the painter, a language that exceeds the sequence of words to be found in a dictionary.

Certainly this new and fruitful approach to painting is by no means only a reaction against photography. It is an all-over revolution against the standards set by positivism, whose creed was formulated by Courbet—"Painting is an essentially concrete art and can consist only in the representation of real and existing things. An abstract, non-visible, non-existent object is not in the domain of painting."[11] no longer coincided with the sensibility and the concept of nature of the younger generation. Nature was no longer limited by sensorial perception, and the series of adjectives, which Courbet had put so alluringly one after the other—abstract, non-visible, non-existent, with the secret intention to read "thus" in the place of each comma—was no longer conclusive for painters like Van Gogh, Gauguin, Seurat, and Redon.

It was Vincent van Gogh who most clearly formulated this new vision of a wider and deeper reality: "To express hope by a star. The ardor of a being by the radiance of a setting sun. This is certainly not the realism of a *trompe l'oeil,* but is it not a thing that really exists?"[12] Here, nature is conceived of in a wider sense than that which visual perception permits us to see, and at the same moment the key word of this young generation appears: expression. And expression calls for a language, for analogies and metaphors, for all the human means of communication which enable mankind to communicate even the invisible. In this generation, at the close of the nineteenth century, a new concept of painting as a language for a new reality was created.

The generation that concentrated on this search can be compared to the encyclopedists: but they did not only strive to compile a dictionary, they endeavoured to find the laws of pictorial language. The analysis of pictorial means now gained an overwhelming importance, as the painters of this generation considered themselves no longer bound to the material facts which sensorial perception offered them in visual reality. The field of reality had been enlarged, and it became the task of painting—as Paul Klee was to formulate it somewhat later—"not to render the visible, but to make visible."

Kandinsky was one of the first great artists of this century to concentrate on this analysis of pictorial means. And he was the first to consider this analysis in a general pattern of spiritual values: by stressing the "principle of internal necessity," he builds the framework within which the grammar of pictorial language acquires sense and meaning: "Generally speaking, color directly influences the soul. Color is the keyboard, the eyes are the hammers, the soul is the piano with many strings. The artist is the hand that plays, touching one key or another purposively to cause vibrations in the soul. It is evident therefore that color harmony must rest ultimately on purposive playing upon the human soul; this is one of the guiding principles of internal necessity."[13]

The principle of internal necessity is the ground from which all artistic creation springs, but it is also the source of every language, the origin of every articulate communication between human beings. This is even more true when this communication is not limited to the mere and factual task of "notification" or of an exchange of practical signals, but when it rises to the level of real communication, that is to say the need of a human being to share his emotions, his experience, his thoughts and contemplations with his fellow human beings. Therefore, the chapter which immediately follows the statement of the "principle of inner necessity" in Kandinsky's book, *Concerning the Spiritual in Art (Über das Geistige in der Kunst)*, is called the "Language of Form and Color". This is an analysis of form and color, meant to be the essay of a pictorial grammar based on the analogy with music, but also with language.

Kandinsky in a previous chapter had given his attention to the double significance of the word— the element of poetical language: "The word is an inner sound. It springs partly, perhaps principally, from the object denoted. But if the object is not seen, but only its name heard, the mind of the hearer receives an abstract impression only of the object dematerialized, and a corresponding vibration is immediately set up in the 'heart'."[14] Here he already defines a difference between the function of the word as a notation referring to factual reality, and another value of the word, apt to serve poetical aims by the evocation of an image, which is still linked up with reality and association, but no longer with sensorial perception.

"A word which has two meanings, the first direct, the second indirect, is the material of poetry and literature, which these arts alone can manipulate and through which they speak to the soul."[15] The parallel of the word and its double significance to "form" in the domain of the visual arts is evident: form can have a relation to factual reality, but it can be used, as well, by its direct, immediate appeal to the "human heart": "The organic form here no longer serves as direct object but is only an element of the divine language, which needs human expression because it is directed from man to man."[16] Kandinsky showed the veracity of his theoretical statements in a series of paintings, which are about contemporary to the publication of his book *Über das Geistige in der Kunst*: forms, taken from the world of visible reality, are modified and integrated into resounding compositions, that owe their life and vivacity by no means to the associative reference to visible reality, but in the first instance to the immediate value of their "sound" in the rhythm and sense of the entire composition (Fig. 2). "Nature is only a dictionary"—and Kandinsky was the first to choose his words from this dictionary in complete freedom.

Kandinsky once used this word: a dictionary. Stating that attempts to constitute a pictorial theory are doomed to shipwreck, he continued: "However, it would be rash to say that there are no principles in painting comparable to a foundation, or that such principles would inevitably lead to academicism. Music has a grammar which, although modified from time to time, is of continual help and value and may be used as a kind of dictionary."[17]

In his approach to the analysis of his art, Kandinsky held a very high opinion of the artist's task: "The artist must have something to communicate, since mastery over form is not the end but, instead, the adapting of form to internal significance."[18] For him, the artistic communication acquired the rank of a message. If this message is to be conveyed clearly and distinctly, a language is necessary as a means of communication. Language in itself is not art but a semantic system, a means of communication, enabling man to address a message to his brother. And as a system, it needs a certain amount of conventions, of objective facts. So does painting. In order to establish these facts, the generation of Kandinsky turned toward the analysis of the means, which up to that time had been handled more or less traditionally, without a precise knowledge of the importance and scope of these means. In speaking of the artist who seeks to apply the means of music to his own art, Kandinsky said: "Comparison of means among the arts and the learning of one art from another can only be successful when the application of the lesson is fundamental. One art must learn how another used its method, so that its own means may then be used according to the same fundamental principles, but in its own medium. The artist must not forget that each means implies its proper application and that it is for him to discover this application."[19]

It was the attempt toward a conscious use of the pictorial elements, which had by now been freed from their absolute servitude to visual perception, that led toward the constitution of a pictorial grammar. The clearest example of this tendency is the introductory course, the *Vorkurs*, of the Bauhaus, created by Johannes Itten, and sponsored by Kandinsky and Paul Klee, who both showed an ever-increasing interest in the principles of artistic language. But the *Vorkurs* is an introduction to art, a *gradus ad Parnassum*, and not an artistic accomplishment, as a whole group of epigones seem to think nowadays; the exercises of the *Vorkurs* are *études* in the most precise sense of the word—and certainly the *étude* can be raised to the rank of an artistic creation, but only by a man of such genius as Chopin. For Kandinsky and the masters of the Bauhaus, the *Vorkurs* had a precise aim: to serve as a linguistic base for artistic creation, as a grammar for a language to be handled by an artist: "Painting is an art; and art is not vague production, transitory and isolated, but a power which must be directed to the development and refinement of the human soul. . . . No other power can take the place of art in this activity. And sometimes when the human soul is gaining greater strength, art also grows in power, for the two are inextricably connected and complementary."[20]

The development and refinement of the human soul—this is the task Kandinsky was allotting to the visual arts—the artist becomes a teacher of humanity, a prophet of spiritual harmony and happiness, and his language—distorted as it may be by the impact of a prophecy—is needed to convey a message to the other members of human society. For this reason the means of artistic expression are no longer conceived of—as had been the tradition through several centuries—as means of representation, as ways of connotation of an independent reality. The industrial revolution of the visual arts set them free to become linguistic symbols; to become means of expression according to the "principle of internal necessity", which reigns over every spoken or painted language.

In the recent history of the visual arts, another instance can be shown, where the interest in the linguistic structure of the elements of painting springs from an equally high and lofty principle as in the case of Kandinsky: it is the group and the common activity of the members of *de Stijl*. The painters of this group: Mondrian, Van der Leck and Van Doesburg, concentrated on the research of the linguistic elements in painting as early as 1917, the year of the founding of the group. In fact during the preceding years they were already making preliminary studies, leading the way toward a new conception of painting as a language. Indeed, the masters of *de Stijl* found their way to each other by the fact that they were about the only painters in the Netherlands who saw the predominant importance of this way of approach.

Fig. 4. Bart Van der Leck. *Stag* (drawing).   Fig. 5. Bart Van der Leck. *Stag* (drawing).

At least one of them, Mondrian, had been prepared for this linguistic discipline by Cubism. In this movement, the addiction to the austere and dominating spirit of syntaxis, of composition, had indeed created a new climate, that shows clearly in all the paintings of the Cubist artist, and is formulated in words by Georges Braque: *"J'aime la règle qui corrige l'émotion."* This attitude of rigorous discipline is evident in the paintings of the Cubist group: a few objects—the violin, the guitar, the glass and the pitcher —are the objects on their canvases. But they are of no autonomous importance: they only serve to exemplify the syntaxis, the way of composition, the Cubists had proffered. Not the violin or the glass—or any other object—is the content of their paintings, but the "mental operations" to which Valéry had referred, the structure and the system of a pictorial language. That is the reason why Juan Gris could state the difference between Cubism and the former schools of painting in the following manner: "Artists believed to be able, with beautiful models or beautiful motifs, to arrive at a poetic end. We believe, rather, in attaining this with beautiful elements, for those of the spirit are certainly the most beautiful."[21]

This hint toward a spiritualistic concept of the world was still not sufficient for the masters of *de Stijl*. In their attempt at an utter purification of the visual arts, they were to go further. And their Dutch origin—contrary to the predominantly French descent of the Cubist painters—conferred on them an additional trend of iconoclastic orthodoxy. The painters of *de Stijl* were in search of the absolute: universal harmony. And in order to depict universal harmony, no individual form of the creation is admissible, as they all would be only a fragment—and therefore a distortion—of the absolute. All these fragmentary forms were thus to be exiled from their paintings, as being an offense to the absolute—quite in the same way that in Holland in the sixteenth century all the images and sculptures of saints were removed from the churches, as they were considered an offense against absolute sanctity. In order to exclude every possibility of subjective arbitrariness, apt to be a distortion of the absolute harmony, the masters of *de Stijl* limited the means of expression in their painting to the very minimum (Fig. 3) as far as form was concerned: to the straight line and to the right angle, that is to say to the vertical and horizontal line; as to color: to the three primary colors (yellow, blue and red) and the primary non-colors (black, white and gray). On this very limited stock of linguistic elements they built their language, stressing by this fact the importance of the "mental operations". For it was the spiritual content of their paintings, the rendering of universal harmony, that excluded any handling of the language other than by a procedure of adequate spirituality; the "mental operations" of this art entered into the linguistic domain of mathematics. There

146

Fig. 6. Bart Van der Leck. *Stag* (watercolor).　　　　　　　　　　Fig. 7. Bart Van der Leck. *Stag*.

is a very relevant parallel between the works of *de Stijl* and their linguistic attitude on one hand, and the writings of Spinoza on the other: in their way of approach to the pictorial language, the paintings of *de Stijl* show the same preoccupation with objectivity and clean transparency as Spinoza's masterwork, which is called *Ethica more geometrico demonstrata*. I have ventured elsewhere that one could well apply this title to the collective *oeuvre* of *de Stijl*.

But the idea of language, as a primary constituent of the life of painting, dominated not only in the narrow circle of the addicts of *de Stijl*. It penetrated many other artists, and even the heretics of *de Stijl* could not liberate themselves from this constant reflection. Bart Van der Leck was the outstanding example of this attitude. Very early in the history of *de Stijl* he rejected the abstract philosophical creed of his friends, and turned again to figurative painting. But his concern for objectivity, for the discipline of pictorial language, remained intact, and the creative process of his painting is indeed a translation in the most precise sense of the word. More than an abstraction, his metamorphosis of a perceptual form into a linguistic sign is a translation into a conceptual language, which is much more important than the visible forms from which the artist deducted and abstracted. A series of Van der Leck's drawings, watercolors and paintings (Figs. 4–7) is a decisive demonstration of the domination of language above the forms of sensorial perception, which, in Van der Leck's *oeuvre*, do not constitute anything more than the raw material, from which the final composition has been derived. Whereas in the work of the other masters of *de Stijl*, these perceptions do not even serve as raw material, the starting point being an all-over vision of nature, thus rendering the dictionary of nature quite superfluous. Van der Leck's work, however, though reverting to this dictionary, is an example of the tendency toward a linguistic structure in painting. At the same time it is a brilliant proof of the creative power of the artist, who not only creates a new language, but succeeds from the very first in employing this language for the purpose of art, that is to say, in order to convey a message of meaning and sense.

The panorama of contemporary art seems nowadays not at all dominated by the tendencies which I have tried to delineate in rough lines in the paragraphs of this essay. Contemporary painting and sculpture seem, on the contrary, under the spell of a quite different spirit: the emphasis, in our days after the Second World War, falls on the dionysiac exclamation, on the eruption of sound and emotion—that is to say on the contrary of the structural approach to painting. For the emotional yell, the ecstatic eruption of gestures and brushstrokes does not call for a linguistic discipline—it is a message that does not need articulate language.

Still, there exists within the panorama of post-war art at least one typical example which demonstrated a new form of the linguistic approach: the figurines of the sculptor Robert Jacobsen (Fig. 8). And it is a relevant fact that these figurines are a sideline in the work of an abstract sculptor who has, in his spatial constructions, developed a grammar of new language for sculpture. But in these figurines we see a quite different result come to light: the metaphoric use of sculptural words. "Nature is only a dictionary" —but that does not imply that words found in this dictionary cannot be employed by a vivid and versatile imagination in a sense that has not been listed in the book. This is what constantly happens in Jacobsen's work: he finds words, like screw-caps, bolts, switches, and uses them according to analogy or to a metaphoric need, for eyes, noses, legs, joints etc. Nature may well be a dictionary, but human imagination, the way to convey a message to other men, is by no means limited to the conventional language that is listed in the dictionary; it has, always and anew, the possibility to enlarge, to refashion, the spoken language, to animate it with the needs and the urges of the period.

The pictorial language, however, has remained a fact of importance ever since the beginning of this century. It may be considered as the pre-eminently social element in painting, because language and communication are closely linked to the contact of man with his fellow human being. And the emphasis which, in the last sixty to eighty years, has been put on the linguistic aspects of painting, may well be the result of a renewed consciousness of the social implications and possibilities of the visual arts, which Vincent van Gogh so strongly felt when writing: "the more I think about it, the more I feel that there is nothing more really artistic than to love people."[22]

1. André Gide—Paul Valéry, *Correspondence 1890-1942,* Paris, Gallimard (1955) pp. 355-356.
2. Charles Baudelaire, *L'Art Romantique,* Jacques Crepet ed., Paris (1925) p. 9.
3. Gustave Flaubert, *Correspondence 1852-1854,* Paris (1927) p. 18.
4. John Rewald, *Georges Seurat,* Paris, Albin Michel (1948) pp. 121-122.
5. Maurice Denis, *Théories 1890-1910,* Paris (1912) p. 1.
6. Baudelaire, *op. cit.,* p. 305.
7. *Idem,* p. 8.
8. *Idem,* pp. 9-10.
9. *Idem,* p. 15.
10. Charles Baudelaire, *Curiosités esthétiques,* Jacques Crepet ed., Paris (1923) pp. 268-269.
11. Pierre Courthion, *Gustave Courbet raconté par lui même,* Geneva (1950) pp. 205-206.
12. Vincent van Gogh, *Verzamelde brieven,* Amsterdam, Wereld Bibliotheek (1952-54) Vol. III, p. 295, letter 531.
13. Wassily Kandinsky, *Concerning the spiritual in art and painting in particular, 1912,* translated from the German by Ralph Manheim, New York, Wittenborn, Schultz, Inc. (1947) p. 45.
14. *Idem,* p. 34.
15. *Idem,* p. 34.
16. *Idem,* p. 48, note 6.
17. *Idem,* p. 67.
18. *Idem,* p. 75.
19. *Idem,* p. 40.
20. *Idem,* p. 74.
21. In *de Stijl,* Vol. II, p. 101.
22. Van Gogh, *op. cit.,* Vol. III, p. 308, letter 538.

Fig. 8. Robert Jacobsen. *Figurine*.

One can consider art to be essentially identifiable as invention. The invention of means of expression; the first thrust into realms which contain as yet unknown aesthetic and formal possibilities.

That is the sense in which art presupposes something novel. The newness of the idea, newness of the themes, newness of the form. This kind of newness can be achieved in two ways: (a) in an individual way—which has its origin in the intellectual and psychological make-up of the artist; (b) in a more general way—which bases itself on experimenting with objective possibilities of form. In an extreme case (a) will lead to 'art informel' or to a neo-dadaistic combination of materials; (b) leads to structure. On the one hand: materials in their "natural" condition, individually interpreted. On the other: tectonic laws which ultimately are schematically applied in a uniform distribution.

Even though amorphous material can be considered to possess an inner configuration—a structure of its own—in its natural condition, we can eliminate this kind of structure from our consideration, for as an inherent structure it is not accessible to aesthetic or visual arguments, either in painting or in sculpture.

Tectonic laws are altogether different. They are accessible to aesthetic arguments for they are principally laws of order, and in the end art = order. In other words, art is neither a surrogate for nature, nor for individuality, nor for spontaneity. And where it appears as such, it is art only insofar as it informs the surrogate with order and form. Because order is so characteristic of art, art begins to rely for order on the tectonic laws.

Now the question arises as to what a tectonic law, a law of order, as we know it in science, means with respect to art. That is, where does structure end and art begin?

Let us start with the extreme case: a plane is covered with a uniform distribution in the sense in which this is understood in statistics; or a uniform network extends into space. This is an order which could be uniformly extended without end. Such an order we here call a structure. In a work of art, however, this structure has its limits, either in space or on the plane. Here we have the basis for an aesthetic argument in the sense that a choice has to be made: the possible, aesthetically feasible extension of the structure. Actually it is only through this choice to limit the arbitrarily extensible structure on the basis of verifiable arguments that a discernible principle of order becomes comprehensible.

But is a choice, or the setting of limits, sufficient for the creation of a work of art? This question arises mainly because, since the radical attempt to dispense with all individualistic stylistic expression beginning with Mondrian, no reduction can be extreme enough. This also arises because the aesthetic information offered by the means of expression is dwindling sharply: *neither locatable nor measurable, neither expressing nor indicating an order:* producing a neuter with aesthetic pretensions. The aesthetic quality is beginning to withdraw into the most extreme reductions, into the most extreme objectivity, culminating ultimately in the negation of newness and of invention.

But invention always presupposes the discovery of new problems. The discovery of these new problems is individually determined. Art is unthinkable without the effort of the individual. Order on the other hand is impossible without an objectifying structure.

This means that art can originate only when and because individual expression and personal invention subsume themselves under the principle of order of the structure and derive from it a new lawfulness and new formal possibilities.

Such lawfulness and such inventions manifest themselves as rhythm in an individual case. Rhythm transforms the structure into form; i.e. the special form of a work of art grows out of the general structure by means of a rhythmic order.

Max Bill. *Rhythm in Space*, 1947-48.

Richard Lippold. *Flight*, 1963. Pan-Am Building, New York.

Structure is illusion. The greatest wonder of the many wonders of this century is this fact. For the first time in his history, man is able to prove—or at least is on the verge of proving—that all of the means he has ever used to define the nature of nature and thus his own nature, is the illusion afforded him by his meager senses and sensitivities. His ever-changing definitions, calculations, analyses, measurements, descriptions, propositions, proofs, answers, certainties—even uncertainties and questions: all are illusion. Even the disillusion so produced becomes illusion. A few decades ago such utterances might have come only from an Eastern mystic, surely not from a Western artist, let alone a Western scientist; yet I, as a Western artist, base these remarks not on the currently fashionable mystique of Zen Buddhism, but on the almost identical findings, if different phrasings, of Western science.

It can almost be said that this age of disillusion is in reality an age of dissolution. The rapid succession of theories destroyed by science has left even the scientist with grave doubts as to the meaning of *anything* beyond its own momentary mention. A young Nobel Prize scientist, still in his twenties, speaking recently at a Massachusetts Institute of Technology symposium, said that things were happening so fast in physics these days that he could not understand at all what the "younger" men were talking about.

On what is this dissolution based? Insofar as I, as a layman, can understand it (although as an artist I have long "known" it), what seems to have happened to an understanding of the structure of matter (the same process applies to psychic, social, and philosophical structures as well) is that with every effort to describe it from one point of view, a new point of view manifests itself. Just when the most minute particle, for example, has been described for us, it seems to disappear, or at least to transfer its "true" existence to some other area of "reality"—from physical matter to electrical energy, for instance. Recently even the smallest electrical particle has been assumed to be a tiny bit of whirling space, inexplicably thrown into a dervish-like vortex, emanating energies as by-products whose illusory forms (waves, electrical impulses) we interpret as "matter" through our limited perceptions. We have come, since my childhood, from the "knowledge" that we are chemically ninety-five percent water to the "certainty" that we are physically one hundred percent "empty" space!

However, it may only seem to our impoverished intelligences that the tiny vortexes of our atomic "structure" are whirling, or are even what we call Space. Even if they can be said to be whirling, we know now that movement is relative, and their speed may be such that they are also standing still, as we are told *we* would be if we "traveled" at the speed of light. Or their movement in space, which we now "know" is infinite and endless, would imply that they really are going nowhere, because there is no "where". We can no longer ask "where" or "when". (As I write this, an astronaut has just flown out of February twenty-first into February twentieth and back again, not only once, but several times! If we cannot say "where" he is or "when" he is, can we even ask "what" he is?) On the one hand then, we seem to have come empirically to the same point of view as the religious one which has warned us for a long time that "all is vanity."

On the other hand, no sooner has all matter, all identity of place and time thus vanished into the greater "void" of space, than science suspects, by observing nature's penchant for symmetry, that space cannot be empty. Apparently it seems "empty" only because of our meager access to its "total" properties. Space is now supposedly *stuffed* with conjectured, therefore as yet immeasurable, Matter

and Anti-matter. We are, according to recent reports, merely the lucky (or unlucky) debris of a constant warfare between this Matter and Anti-matter, which fills up the interstices of a space whose most minimal, detectable particles are merely a kind of dead residue of the battle. We are like the slower lemmings who escape suicide through native lethargy—or at least our atomic particles are, if we still wish, as "whole" men, to remain blameless in this newer situation. Yet it must seem small comfort that we "exist" because our most minute particles are either ashes or pacifists.

Again we are confronted by a new version of a familiar duality: all or nothing. Like previous alternatives, innocence or experience, grace or disgrace, they provide for the return of guilt through doubt.

But are they alternatives? Is perhaps "all" also "nothing" and "nothing" also "all"? To swing for a moment a few degrees on the inflexibly mounted axis of human perception, the seeming alternative can be viewed in another way. The alternative exists because what we call Nature is always posing paradoxes. As has been pointed out, Nature has a penchant for symmetry, but she has as much a penchant against it, by means of the chance effects of the inter-relation of all things. So the "laws" of Nature which seem to cause each member of her family to establish its unique identity (we plant an acorn; we do not get a monkey), are modified by the accidents which befall existence (rains may sweep away the nut, enemies consume, or friends nourish it). The "law" is the ideal form (the potential "void" of static, timeless space), "chance" is the modifier of the ideal (the unseen warfare of Matter and Anti-matter, charging and shaping "space").

Together, the peace *and* the war, the empty *and* the full, are responsible for the existence of form.

Thus has science, at long last, later than art and philosophy, brought us face to face with the necessity to see that we cannot choose between the empty and the full and pretend to be alive, because they are the same thing. I have attempted to express this situation visually by four of the six pages in the center of this article.

The first two pages are white ("empty") and the last two pages are black ("full"). In graphic terms, these are as opposite qualities as I am able to produce to make my point. But in actuality what are they? Of course the white pages are "inexperienced", and the black pages are "experienced", full to the point of literal saturation. No room is left for another event. In relation to the consideration of matter in science as I referred to it above, the white pages are like the seemingly pure state of absolute space, of the "nothing" whose self-movements may generate energy; and the black pages are the material sediment of all the apparent energy which fills the void of non-being: a dense, solid, tangible mass of total "stuff". But are they? Or, more properly, is it?

The answer is self-evident: the white pages are stuffed to the full with "emptiness", while the black pages are deliciously void of "nothing". Thus each is equally empty and equally full. There is no choice as to condition. Even if we attempt to choose on the basis of white and black alone, who can say, except from prejudice, that white is empty, is nothing, and black is full, is everything? Or vice versa? All we can attempt to say is that white is the absence of black, and black is the absence of white; by this very implication the existence of the other is assured.

If, then, both are possible, yet neither is sufficient, it would seem, as I began by stating, that if only paradox is "real", all other "reality", or form, is illusion.

We in the West particularly have been prone to accept the deceits of "calculable" or "definable"

155

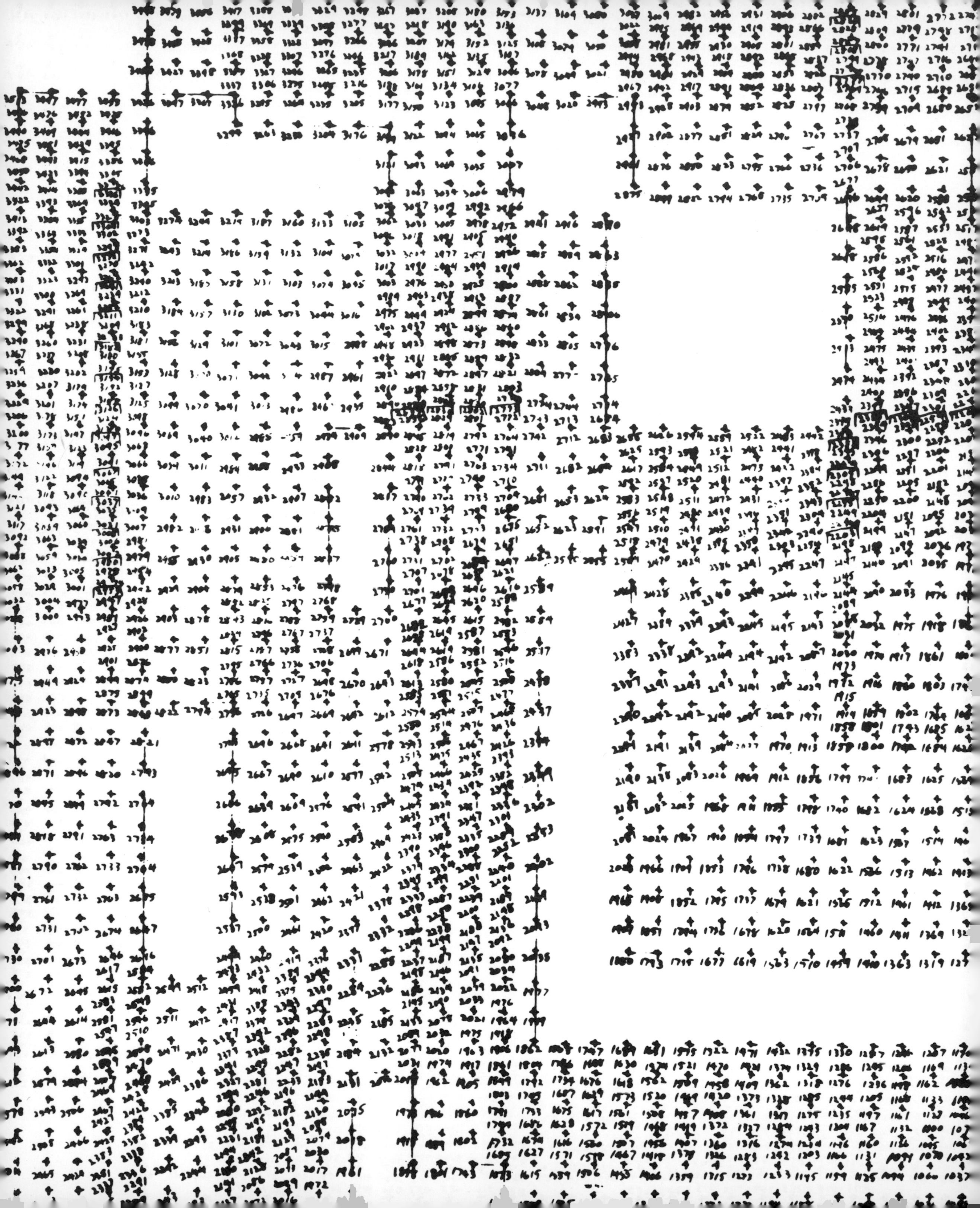

structures and to defend them to the death. As seen in the arts, we have insisted on every conceivable "truth" about form, from the security of the "mass" of the pyramids to the security of "pure space" in the empty walls of an Yves Klein exhibition, with, of course, every imaginable variant and combination to suit our changing concepts. (Yet a close look at "mass" reveals that even the densest metal is so full of "space" that all kinds of energies pass through it unimpeded. Cosmic rays and television shows pass through any mountain—as well as the "mass" of our own bodies—quite freely. As for "pure space": a cubic centimeter of the space in Mr. Klein's "emptiness" has enough cosmic energy in it to populate a universe.)

We have embraced symmetry as an ideal and we have rejected it as an empty conceit. We have reduced vision to a calculated formula of constructed elements, and rejected it for an "automatic" compilation of the debris of order. Who of us has been "right"? "Neither, said the moon" (said Emily Dickinson), "That is best which is not . . ." Not mass, not void; not anything in between. Not symmetry, not law, not disorder, not chaos; not anything in between. Only NOTHING . . .

But NATURE! we cry. NATURE is not *Nothing!* NATURE has evidence for whatever we wish to believe! NATURE *loves* symmetry; look at the human body, or a snowflake; read this news item: "Sundsvall, Sweden, July 27 (AP)—Two cars of the same make and the same color collided head-on outside Sundsvall. Both drivers were thrown against their cars' windshields and were treated at the local hospital for cuts. One driver was Finn Gagner, aged twenty-five. The other was Dag Gagner, twenty-five. They are identical twins. . . ." What a magnificent, symmetrical, orderly event!—except that it was, of course, an accident.

For those who seek to prove it, Nature can be said to *hate* symmetry. Look *closely* at the right side and the left side of a face; no two snowflakes are ever identical; chance events are the only real determiners of character, from the shape and size of a tree to the "choice" of one's love.

But these are the very clues to our contemporary feelings about structure. Symmetry is an accident of disorder, yet accident is the order of non-symmetry—what Hans Arp calls the "Laws of Chance", or the scientist approximates with his "Second Law of Thermodynamics." The wildest of neo-Dada "happenings" can be as carefully calculated and reconstructed as a master plan for the sewers of New York City. In fact, since there is no "time" and "space", *all* events and objects are merely immediate sensations. Order is but an event of the briefest duration, for nothing is identical from moment to moment. The warfare of Matter and Anti-matter is in us all, growth and decay rotate in their orbits as steadily and simultaneously as Venus and Mars about the Sun, pursuing and pursued. What can be left but staticity and the total "mass" of nothingness? Obviously what can be left can just as well be called everythingness. It is true that Nature is not only Nothing; Nature is also Everything.

In the face of this totality, revealed for us now by Science as well as by Philosophy and Religion (in this sense, Science *becomes* our contemporary Philosophy and Religion), how can this be made visible, sensible to our human equipment?

Between the white pages and the black pages in this article are two pages carrying a cryptic diagram. Into the space of the white pages have filtered energetic particles of black, or one can say that the space of the black pages has fissured, and whiteness has isolated the particles of black, like a gigantic magnification, revealing the inner "structure" of black. Because of this "space", as in the mountain or the metal, the "solid" black has only been an illusion all along. Referring back to the white pages, we can say the same. This is a magnification of them also, revealing the invisible energies inherent in what seems to be pure space, like Matter and Anti-matter made visible.

It will be noted on close inspection, that there is an "order" to the little particles, yet it is as deceptive an order, in its relation to "reality", as is the order of the chaotic struggle of Matter and Anti-matter in relation to the form of shapes in space. Its deception lies in the fact that this diagram is part of a study for a piece of sculpture which in its finished state is never seen to have the symmetry and systematic arrangement of this, its inner "structure". I have chosen to leave the drawing unidentified, because the sculpture exists and is experienced on its own terms beyond this part of its creation, much as we exist and relate to what we call "life" beyond and in addition to the interstices of our atomic structures, the vacancies in our psyches, the silences in our senses, and the various energies which occupy all of these in part.

This drawing then, is both something *and* nothing; it is black *and* white, it is empty *and* full. It is as "abstract" as the principles behind the operation of all things, and it is as "real" as the operation of those principles. It is a visual set of laws which in the finished sculpture are broken by the "accidents" of four-dimensional existence, of light, of point of view, and of perspective. It is also, conversely, the accident of a particular artist's vision in a particular moment in "history", thus becoming a specific, identifiable entity, a "law"—a formula for these particular chance occurrences.

In all these respects, this drawing and the kind of sculpture which it represents, is relevant to the point of view to which Science is bringing us, and which frees us for the first time from decision as well as from indecision. Without "time", we have all of Time; with all of Space, we have no need to choose a particular "space". Like this sculpture, we know the "mass" of space, and the "movement" of staticity; for, although the sculpture's own movement, or activity between its parts, or human movement in relation to it may or may not exist, its very being in a state of relationship is no more nor less than the great staticity of all universal events at a given instant, and, as I have already pointed out, at the very next instant everything will be (apparently) different again. Another static moment will have appeared, and, together with the first, will be assumed to be movement by our feeble perceptions and the deceptions of memory. Like all assumptions, this is illusion.

It is quite true that our arrival at a point of no decision in the arts and sciences, more or less simultaneously at this "moment", is in itself another illusion. True to human form, the general awareness of this illusion at this juncture has effected another choice: acceptance of the illusion, or rejection of it (which is to say acceptance of disillusion). But it is quite natural that in being free *from* decision, we are at once free *for* it as well. Our "moment" still triumphs!

The proof of this paradox is visible in the world of sculpture, as I have already pointed out. The decision to abandon law and order, as in the selection of debris and automatism, leads at once to the proscribed law of anarchy—a law none-the-less, and inviolable in the direction of any "outer" law. The decision to employ pristine materials and "orderly" procedures, "free" from predetermined forms and processes, exposes it to the hazards of the evolution of its own growth, and the distortions of external efforts, like the "growth" of all living things in Nature. Which is free, and which slave?

Seen in this light, works evolved from interests described above operate either as protest (through disillusion) or as illustration (through dedicatory illusion) of the same current attitudes. The black is contained in the white; the white is possessed by the black. All structure in contemporary sculpture, to be a part of this "static" moment, must be a part of this new illusion, just as sculptural structures of the "past" were a part of the illusions of those moments. "Ultimate Reality" is so far removed still from our awareness that we have only contemporary illusions on which to erect our forms. It is irrelevant whether they come from science or from somewhere else. The delight of science at this point is its surprise with its discovery that it too is only a small illusion in the mind of man.

In this way, the scientist, the artist, and the prophet are one, for it is the general acceptance of a particular illusion which motivates and unifies mankind at any given time. To abandon this illusion to chaos or to embrace previous illusions is to die. Creativity, like life and like love, depends on a man's ability to accept an illusion, to be aware of it, and to sustain it. Only in this way can he find a structure for his life and for his work. Illusion *is* structure.

MARGIT STABER

CONCRETE PAINTING
AS STRUCTURAL PAINTING

The concept of structure is of central importance for an understanding of what is called concrete art in contemporary visual arts. Our discussion of this subject will be limited to painting, where the phenomenon of structure lends itself to a particularly clear demonstration.

Concrete Art: This designation was introduced in 1930 by Theo van Doesburg. He and a number of like-minded painter friends founded a group and magazine by that name in order to give a programmatic as well as firm theoretic basis to the new artistic conceptions which up until that time had appeared under the most contradictory nomenclature—one spoke (and still does today) of absolute, non-objective, non-representational, abstract, and finally of "entirely abstract" art. Van Doesburg subsumed under the term concrete those trends of the new art in which all gradations of abstraction had been overcome and in which previously unknown pictorial possibilities were discovered and realized solely through the use of form and color, light and movement, all sorts of different materials and methods, and by means of constructive "structural" laws. He and his friends applied the term concrete to that autonomous method of creation which originated with the pioneer generation of Kandinsky, Kupka, Delaunay, Malevitch, Arp, and Mondrian, whose legitimate heirs they considered themselves to be.

Except for the run-of-the-mill identification of the concept concrete with the notion of something palpable, which, of course, any philosophical dictionary will refute, the pictorial and plastic arts of all periods and stylistic directions, if the term is used precisely, could be called concrete insofar as a creative idea has been transmuted into the reality and sensuousness of the work of art. One can detect this line of thought already in Hegel's *Aesthetik*[1] where he uses the concept of the concrete for the process by which a work of art is actualized. Even though an entirely "non-representational" painting or piece of sculpture could not have been imagined during Hegel's time, his formulations already point to a view of art which is adequate for us. Quite a few of his ideas—taken out of their context—could be applied directly to a description of concrete painting; for instance, the following: "Cleanly drawn lines, which run on without being differentiated, without diverging in this or that direction, smooth surfaces and the like gratify because of their definiteness and their uniformity . . ."; or about the effect of colors: "the actual red is the effective, royal, concrete color in which blue and yellow—which are opposites—permeate each other; green can also be looked upon as being such a unification, not as a concrete unit though, but simply as the difference which has been effaced, as the satiated, tranquil neutrality. These colors are the purest, simplest, the most basic primary colors." Whom would this description not remind of Mondrian?

What Hegel ascertained about the sensuousness of the material of works of art, and the part it plays in the intellectual and psychic effect of these works, has become self-evident since the beginning of the twentieth century, has severed itself from the constraint of the motif, and in this being-purely-itself becomes problematical for the communication between artist and observer. The artists first of all had to ask themselves what it was that was coming into being under their hands, and had to grope toward the formulation of new concepts. Especially the painters made an effort to define what they were doing, in order to justify and explain the miscomprehension their work encountered. The question is whether the thoughts of these painters are a key to an understanding of their work.

Hans Arp, for instance, strictly separated his and Sophie Taeuber's work of the twenties from that of the constructivists whose work "seemed to have affinity with ours"; here it remains to be examined what Arp meant by "constructivists". In his book *Unsern Taeglichen Traum*,[2] which sketches the beginning of his artistic activity, he notes that, together with Sophie Taeuber, he painted, stitched, and glued "probably" the first concrete paintings, in 1915. "These works are self-sufficient, independent realities. They have no rational meaning; they do not have their origin in palpable reality. We disregarded everything that could be considered imitation or description in order to let the elemental and spontaneous have free reign within us. Because the distribution of the planes, their relationships and colors did not have the effect of being consciously determined, I declared that these works had been ordered according to the law of chance. . . ." Concrete painting here has already been assigned a much wider range of effect than is generally assumed.

Generally one thinks of concrete art in connection with Mondrian and Kandinsky, both of whom appropriated the term concrete for their work in their later years. Mondrian, though, notes that this term is just as relative as the designation abstract or "non-figurative". In his opinion, all art is "more or less realism . . . Reality here is understood to be the plastic manifestation of forms and not of events of life."[3] "Neo-plasticism", as Mondrian called his way of painting, was in a certain sense an abstraction of an abstraction, the form and color once more reduced to "straight lines and the exactly determined primary colors" in order to achieve a universal expression which was supposed to determine the general shaping of the environment. The intellectual-aesthetic value of the pictorial composition now resides entirely in the harmony and rhythm of the elements. "Thus the new way of creation is nothing but an aesthetic relationship represented with extreme exactness." But a net of relationships exists within the structural texture, even though Mondrian's pictorial world—these line and color relationships which have been reduced to the utmost—did not come into being by means of an exactly predetermined structure; rather, the pictorial structure was staked out and balanced by means of feeling during the actual process of painting.

Kasimir Malevitch, searching for an art which would correspond to the technological reality, founded "suprematism" in 1913; this was an offshoot of Russian constructivism. Malevitch asked "the reasons for the origin of an artistic structure" and found as his answer the "additive elements"—square, circle, and their derivatives with which he wanted to express, in accordance with the spirit of his time, the feeling of dynamics. "The artist is intent on bringing the additive element into a harmonic norm, into conformity . . ."—"the non-objective world" of art in which feelings and ideas become concrete.[4]

And Paul Klee: he did not like the word art, but preferred the term *Gestaltung*, which was more closely related to the creative process. He felt that the exploration of the surfaces of objects was exhausted: "The object expands beyond its appearance because of our knowledge of what lies behind it." That was why, in his opinion, painting tended more and more to present abstract images: "To be an abstract painter does not mean to abstract from natural, palpable possibilities of comparison, but is based upon . . . the sifting out of pictorially pure relationships." That is how the artist creates a new world, a transposition with the "pictorially suitable means" of the stimuli which he receives from the world outside him. In his *Gestaltungslehre*[5] Klee developed these pictorial means with extraordinary exactness and richness; he thinks in terms of structural relationships; form-generating processes in which abstraction and concreteness intermingle with each other.

This was what some of the painters of the pioneer generation thought about the origin of their

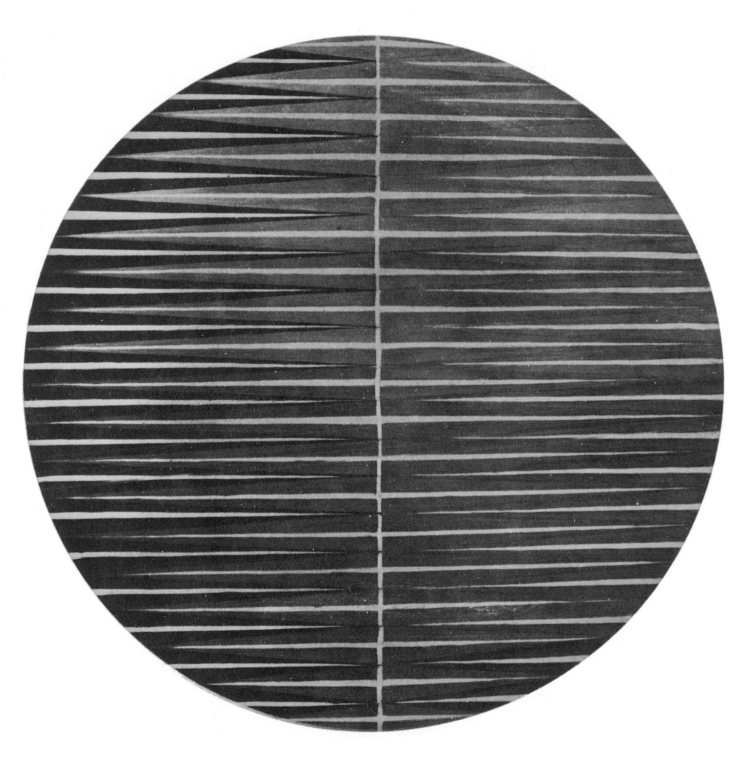

Fig. 1. Giacomo Balla (1911–1958). *Iridescent Conpenetration Number 2*, 1912. Oil on canvas, 77 x 77 cm. Private Collection.

Fig. 2. Piet Mondrian (1872–1944). *Composition: Gray Structure with Color Planes,* 1918. Oil on canvas, 49 x 60.5 cm. Private Collection.

works; the "making" interested them more than the "being". Theo van Doesburg finally formulated the term concrete art for the aforementioned and similar trends; he did this in order to provide them with a principled foundation which would be a guide for future developments. The "Orphism" of Delaunay and Kupka also belongs among the pioneer movements; its articulate theoretician, Guillaume Apollinaire, who gave the movement its name, said: "It is the art to paint new totalities with elements which are not borrowed from visual reality but have been created entirely by the painter himself; he endows them with a persuasive reality of their own. The works of the orphic painters wanted to evoke pure aesthetic pleasure, but at the same time render an easily perceptible structure and a sublime meaning, that is to say, render the subject. That is pure art . . . ."[6] Apollinaire, the poet and interpreter of art, saw the new art on a larger scale than the painters who were struggling with their problems. Theo van Doesburg could make a summarizing statement in the early thirties: "Concrete—not abstract painting, for nothing is more concrete, more real than a line, a color, a surface. For instance, is a woman, a cow, a tree concrete when they are on canvas? No. A woman, a tree are concrete in their natural condition; on canvas they are far more abstract, illusory, undetermined, speculative than a line. . . "[7]

Proceeding from this idea of an objectified, "programmatic" manner of painting, Max Bill— today one of the foremost exponents and theoreticians of concrete art—also undertook to elaborate his basic position and provide it with a theoretic foundation: "Concrete art is the opposite of abstract . . . Concrete is the 'representation' of something that was previously not visible, not palpable . . . The purpose of concretion is to translate abstract ideas into reality so that they can be perceived. . . ." Abstract art, in his opinion, exhibits essential aspects of the world of objects; it extracts systems, modalities, types, principles from the visible world, and looked at from this point of view, every work of art, from antiquity to the present, is an abstraction. Concrete art on the other hand "makes the abstract 'idea-as-such' visible by purely artistic means . . . ,"[8] and the degree of abstraction can go so far that the demarcation between abstract and concrete becomes blurred. Bill gives a much-cited example of this: the red accent on the canvas, which in one instance represents a sunrise in a fog, because of its relationship to the surface also represents an artistic reality.

In the last few years Bill has concentrated especially on the connection between concrete art and structure. He has done this with the intention of destroying the notion of concrete art as a dogmatic, purely geometric, formal canon for which it has been derided, and in order to show that the systems which are available to concrete art possess a mutually wide range of possibilities. For concrete art is still looked upon as only the art of geometric means because the designation, concrete art, was first and expressly used by artists whose works are known as being geometric; the only exceptions besides Max Bill are Hans Arp and Wassily Kandinsky.

One could also take exception to this use of the concept of structure, for it is applicable to all the visual arts and should not be appropriated by one mode alone. For instance, one could think of Renaissance painting with its framework of the central perspective, of the stratified structure of Chinese painting, the geometrizing structure of certain forms of primitive plastic art, or in our time of Morandi's formalizing treatment of the motif. All of these reductions were undertaken so that the meaning and symbolization of these works would be defined more sharply, something that is achieved by emphasizing their diverse structural qualities.

Nevertheless, it seems that the concept of structure is particularly relevant to a mode of work which uses as its only elements pure color and pure form; that is to say, this mode in contrast to other modes is not fully explicable unless the structural qualities are taken into account. For, once an invented object has taken the place of an object which has a realistic frame of reference, the creation of the picture must necessarily rely upon and be secured by autonomous principles of order. Unquestionably, geometry is the main ingredient—geometry in its freest and most complicated form-generating usages, which lead into topology—from the geometric configuration to the representation of the topological space.

The intention to recognize a basic conformity within the complexity of appearances must inevitably have a simplifying effect, as does any inductive method. But this has nothing to do with an oversimplification of the facts. Art exists in the world of its own creations, the uniqueness of its appearance and meaning. Yet this does not exclude the possibility of introducing a clarifying common functional scheme by means of structural methods into a number of formal processes.

Structure in concrete painting is first of all relevant to the formal aspects, that is, to the syntactical connections which, as we have seen, are especially important in an art which does not reflect the exterior world. That means a frame of reference to the aesthetic realities, for the creative idea which has become form is after all the essence of art, and the inner configuration which underlies these forms is also of interest.

We must now differentiate between two aspects of structural thinking which are of interest to painting: 1) the structural description of the work of art; particularly suited to concrete painting, it is valid for every other pictorial expression; 2) the structure as a formal and expressive means itself.

The Structural Description of a Work of Art

In modern, scientifically oriented aesthetics the concept of structure belongs to the basic concepts of the methodical comprehension of aesthetic phenomena. In Germany, particularly Max Bense employs structural methods based on the general theory of symbols, theory of perception, theory of information and communication, in order to develop a system of objective criteria which will have been derived from the work of art itself. There are parallel investigations underway in the United States and in France. In his investigations Bense is influenced by the work of Norbert Wiener, Whitehead, Wittgenstein, Merleau-Ponty, Shannon, Ch. S. Morris, Moles, and Mandelbrot, to name only a few of the many sources which affect aesthetics today. The intention is to reach beyond an interpretation of relationships of colors and forms which depends on the subjective criteria of feelings (the same is true not only for painting but also for other art forms—Bense applies the same categories to literature). The intention is not to eliminate the possibility of interpretation, but to let the ontological approach be preceded by one in which the criteria for perception will first of all produce "value-free" information: degree of order and degree of organization of the means and elements becomes the measure of the degree of invention—something which in turn leads immediately to a value judgment.

Of course, one can also consider the classical approach to interpretation of art—the coordination according to stylistic elements—a structural method, but this system can hardly do without information which is beyond aesthetics. It may result in historically or sociologically important classifications but not in primarily aesthetic classifications. Thus it is another side of the analysis of art, one which is not under discussion here.

Structure as an Artistic Means of Expression

An increasingly structural treatment of pictorial themes becomes noticeable with Cézanne and Cubism. But only in concrete painting does structure appear as a self-sufficient aesthetic process and become an autonomous, creative pictorial law.

This is how Max Bill summarized the formal possibilities inherent in the law of structure: "Concrete art is characterized by one feature: the structure. The structure of the arrangement in the idea, the structure of the visual in the reality, the reality of the structure of the idea, the idea as structure of the reality. And the laws of structure are: the series, the rhythm, the progression, the polarity, the regularity, the inner logic of sequence and arrangement."[9] In general, structurally determined painting is that kind of painting which is based upon a conscious principle of order, upon a controlled and controllable scheme of the process of creation. Besides the geometric and exact elements, amorphous and a-geometric formations are also justified; the sharp and soft contour, sfumato, dissolution into points, formations of nets and fields, the structuring of the actual material used in the painting, the introduction of materials which are "foreign" to the painting, collage, the formation of reliefs, elements of movement, light and shadow systems; in short, all means which can also be used in tachism and lyrical abstraction are applicable in paintings which rely on structural laws.

Structure and Form

There are two approaches to form in concrete painting as structural painting. The first approach we will discuss is that in which the structure is integrated with the image, where the structure so to speak sinks beneath the surface, is latently present and only indirectly discernible. The image as such is so perspicuous that it reaches its full effectiveness independently of the underlying structure. Mondrian (Fig. 2), Klee (Fig. 3), Vantongerloo, Albers (Fig. 4), and Glarner (Fig. 6) all show this approach, as does indeed the example of Max Bill's work shown here (Fig. 8), although many of Bill's paintings belong to the alternate approach to concrete painting which we shall discuss later.

An example by Paul Klee: *Flowering Bed,* 1923 (Fig. 3). Painters chose geometric elements in order to obtain elements which would be especially objective, free of accidental associations, and universally valid. The square was particularly suited for this purpose; of all the geometric forms it is the one which is most symmetrical and regular and as such it is rich in aesthetic properties, but it is also that geometric figure which lets itself be most easily combined and identified. The square not only can serve as the pictorial element, but also as the pictorial structure, pictorial surface, and through a combination of these possibilities become the sole pictorial means. This is a theme to which Klee returned again and again, in spite of the fact that he himself did not employ such exact geometric elements. Yet if one takes Klee's concept of the plane into account, there is only one category of genuine rectangular pictures, that is, only the replete, not the circumscribed plane constitutes a genuine plane (Kandinsky on the other hand endows the circumscriptive line with the capacity to form planes). Thus according to Klee, only color planes can be genuine planes, as for instance in *Flowering Bed*. It consists of approximate color squares which, because of the movement of the color and form, are dynamically directed toward the center: from dark, dull colors to light colors and primary colors permeated with white; from

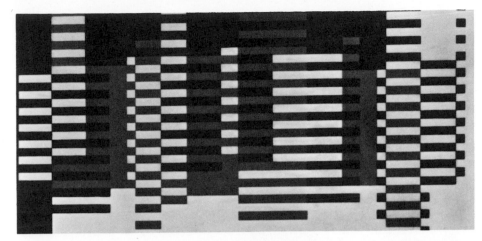

Fig. 4. Josef Albers (born 1888).
City, 1928. Opaque glass, 28 x 55 cm.
Kunsthaus, Zurich.

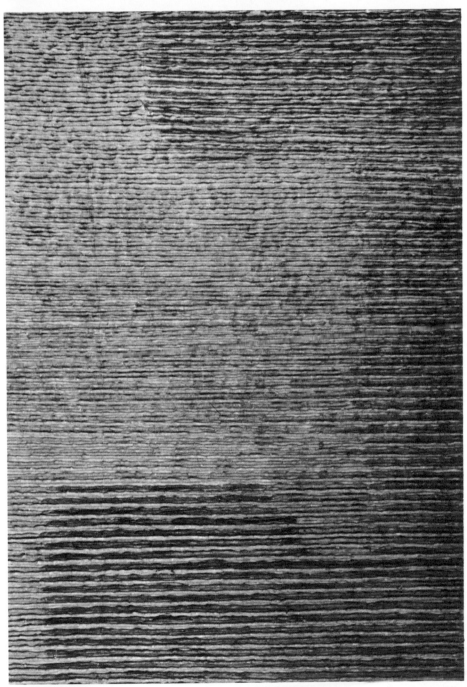

Fig. 5. Wladyslaw Streminsky (1893–1952).
United Composition, 1931/32.
Oil on canvas, 48 x 32 cm.
Museum Sztuki, Lodz (Poland).

Fig. 6. Fritz Glarner (born 1899). *Relational Painting. Tondo Number 21*, 1951. Oil on masonite, diameter 124 cm. Private Collection.

large squares to small squares. Klee calls this "plane activity", something which cannot be understood without knowing his concept of pictorial dimensionality. According to him this activity is achieved through a combination of linear-plane forms with light-dark color values. *Flowering Bed* is exemplary for the form-generating concept Klee had of painting, that is, the representation of movements. Here there is a color movement consisting of a purely structural arrangement which has been achieved through the elemental use of the square; the order is determined by the whole of one pictorial idea.

In the second or alternate approach to form in concrete painting, the structural organization is made visible on purpose and, so to speak, constitutes the character of the form. The painter is intent on showing the relationships of the elements to one another and the network of aesthetic relationships within the structure. This direct "structure painting" can be the result of a very rigorously performed construction—Strzeminsky (Fig. 5), Bill, Lohse, Mavignier, Morellet (Fig. 10), Piene (Fig. 11)—or it can lead away from the construction to its dissolution, i.e. in the direction of informal painting, something which can also be motivated by expressive considerations. Tobey (Fig. 7), Mathieu, Dubuffet show examples of this. As everywhere, the boundaries are not firm here either, the differentiation is difficult, and the ideal definition falls short of reality.

The Italian painter Piero Dorazio offers an excellent example of a mode of structural painting (Fig. 9) in which structure is the formal principle itself. He works with the phenomenon of texture and its aesthetic possibilities, i.e. with a structural principle par excellence. He is interested in the unification of elements which are the same, elements which through the manner in which they are made to interlock acquire a new quality, a quality which is more than that of the single particle. Dorazio stands between the camp to which, for instance, Tobey belongs (the camp which approaches structure from the "organic" side, which is fascinated by the picture of life beneath the surface of appearances— to use a very general classification) and the camp of those who have "programs", who use their means according to strict rules within an exactly predetermined organizational scheme and therewith transmute the "abstract-idea-as-such" into the concretion of the work of art. Dorazio uses forms and colors to break up the tautness of his textures so that they begin to look like finely woven webs; almost unnoticeably he effaces and condenses his structures, leaves certain zones free, bypasses the construction of symmetrical relationships, and acquires a new irreal effect for his paintings which removes them from the rationality of their formal rules. He steers the form by means of color, for the condensation and interweaving of the material is achieved through the use of color, and it is color which develops a radiance, a vibration, and it can develop this only in the structural texture through the intensification of the particle.

Max Bense explains form and structure as the result of different aesthetic conceptions. He says: "An aesthetic conception can come into existence under the aspect of form and under the aspect of structure. . . . Both form and structure are genuine symbolic themes. In each instance the starting point of the theoretical definitions is the symbol. The symbol as a differentiated structure, as element, can be the basis of an integrating aesthetic process; that is how wholeness and form come into existence. But the symbol can also be the basis of a reduplicating process and then structure comes into existence." Bense continues, talking specifically about painting: "In concrete painting the aesthetic conception of 'form' as well as the aesthetic conception of 'structure' (to use the distinction which we have devised)

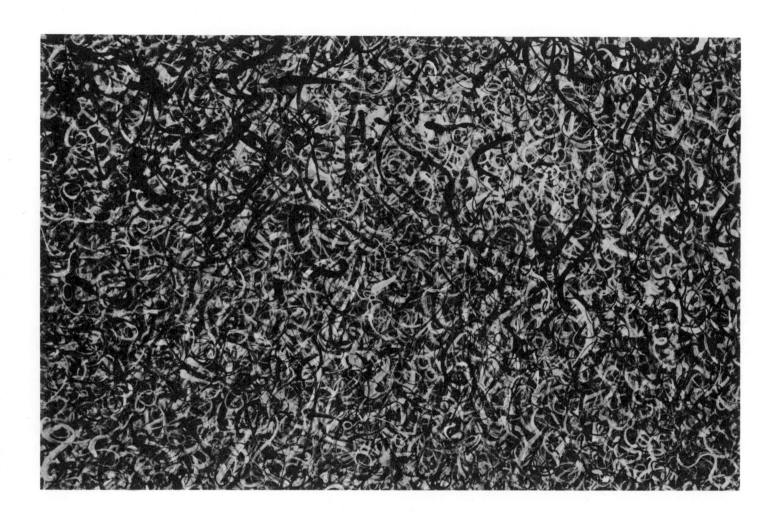

Fig. 7. Mark Tobey (born 1890). *October,* 1957.
Tempera, 71.5 x 112.5 cm. Private Collection.

Fig. 8. Max Bill (born 1908). *Integration of Four Systems,* 1958/59/60.
Oil on canvas, 66 x 66 cm. Private Collection.

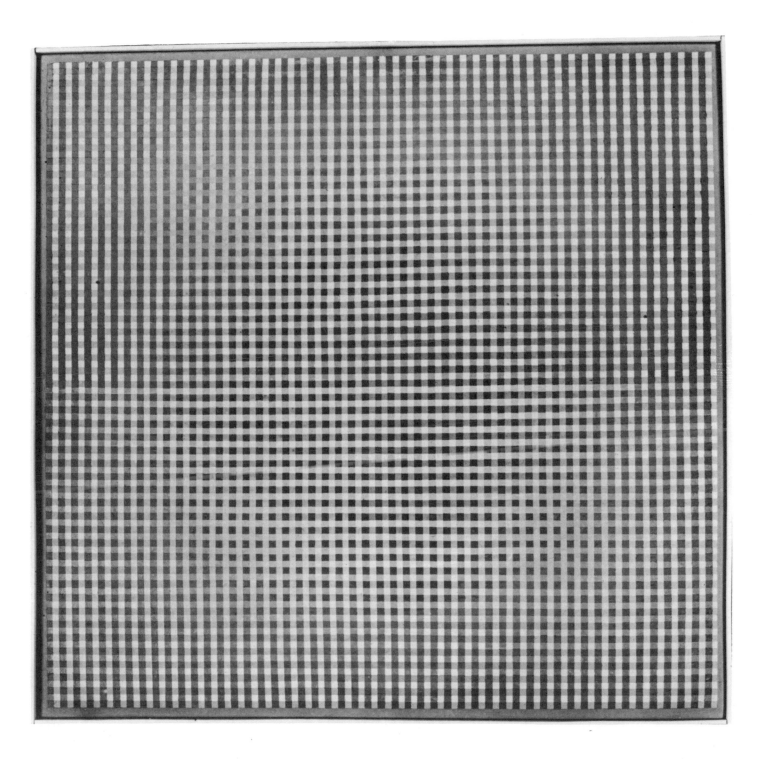

play a productive role." He gives an example of this: "Vordemberge-Gildewart is primarily concerned with the conception of form. But Bill manages to synthesize both kinds of conceptions. The well-known painting *Weisses Quadrat* (1946) is an outstanding example of this kind of synthesis. Here a theme is realized which quite obviously has made a structure-idea the basis of a form-idea. In Mondrian one meets up with similar examples."[10]

In this connection Bense states what the significance of this new mode of painting is: a loss of "semantic information, the aesthetic information nevertheless of relatively high value." That is, what constitutes meaning in the traditional sense is introduced into the relationships of the formal elements themselves. The aesthetic intention which so far had been trapped in a realistic configuration (no matter what shape or form it might have taken) has now been unlocked; now that it is available, one first has to learn to decode it; the grammar of structure offers a chance toward that end.

Max Bill indicates the direction in which, once the syntax has been interpreted, one can look for the pragmatic-semantic effect of concrete art. Kandinsky as well as the group "Art Concret" around van Doesburg had emphasized the social responsibility of the artist and had underlined the fact that especially their art could have an effect on civilization and could breach the gap between art and everyday life. They asserted that a concrete painting, projected in the consciousness of the painter and realized as an objective, self-sufficient pictorial form, was more than simply the equivalent of a personal idea. The primordial pictorial orders represented in concrete painting could be understood as "fulcrums" or "centers of equilibrium", whose objectivity tended to have a broad and general effect. "It is the aim of concrete art to develop psychic objects for intellectual use, similarly to the way in which man creates objects for material utilization." In Bill's opinion, a picture can exert a direct and unconscious influence on the observer, similar to how medicine takes its effect even though the patient is ignorant of what it is composed of or how it has been manufactured. Concrete art succeeds especially well in this endeavour because it is free of all possible representational associations. Conscious confrontation and unconscious radiation constitute the communicative range of such paintings. And this pictorial effect is achieved by intentionally bringing the painting in relationship with space, contrasting the flat image with its environment: the structural image, as part of space, is just as much a self-enclosed nucleus as it is infinitely extendible.

The Concept of Structure in the Natural Sciences

No matter how questionable a comparison between the development of art and that of the natural sciences is, it cannot be denied that since the turn of the century art has begun to orient itself toward within, toward a delicate construction of the material on the one hand and of the pictorial means on the other. The concept of structure was given increased importance at first in connection with the natural sciences; this development was bound up with the increasingly deeper insights into the nature of things which had become possible through better instruments and more refined methods of investigations in physics, mathematics, and biology. The scientific disciplines penetrated into microscopic realms inaccessible to actual representation; in short, attempted to give a structural description of the universe in which the elements and their relation to one another, the inner order, and organization of natural and

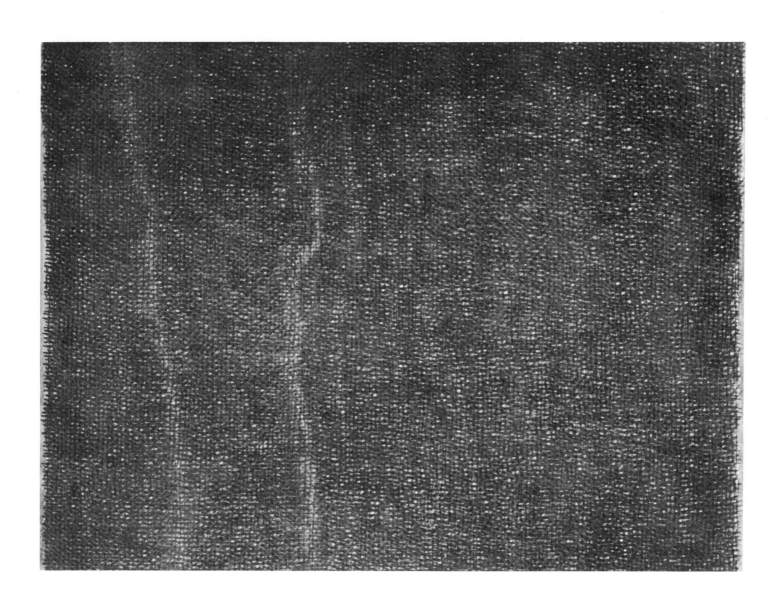

Fig. 9. Piero Dorazio (born 1927). *A Reading in Green*, 1959. Oil on canvas, 90 x 116 cm. Private Collection.

Fig. 10. François Morellet (born 1926). *Dashes 0°–90°*, 1960. Oil on canvas, 80 x 80 cm. Private Collection.

artificial systems come under investigation. In the same manner in art, the immediate relationships between colors, tones, or words—their function as such—have become one of the main interests of creative persons.

Of a much-discussed exhibition "Art and Natural Form" (Basel, 1958) in which photos of microscopic organic and non-organic substances were confronted with non-figurative art, Adolf Portmann had this to say: "It is not as if all the boundaries had been eliminated, as if science and art were about to join forces in a non-figurative world. But the penetration by science of a zone, in which the everyday conceptions are no longer applicable, produces pictures and structural elements similar to those which the artist has discovered for himself through his own experience. The elements of both are equally far removed from the obvious world of objects, but they point in very different directions of intellectual endeavour. . . ." The correspondence between art and science does not simply stem from a similarity in experience, but just as much from the idea that everything can be made, an idea which determines technological thinking and therefore the thinking of modern man. That is why the concept of structure has become so important in art; it was needed to describe a new creative reality and itself became the touchstone for creative thinking, as we have seen. But in what way does the concept of structure in art correspond to the same concept in the sciences, if at all?

Definition of Structure in Science

Kant defined structure as "situation and connection of the parts of an organism which is developing according to a uniform purpose." Wolfgang Wieser, an Austrian, offers a modern formulation; it is not a philosophical one, but was made in reference to a methodological question relating to biological investigations: " 'Structure' should be understood to mean a network of relationships of elements or of elementary processes. Structures appear wherever elements combine into a meaningful whole whose arrangement follows definite laws. The wholeness in which we discover and examine structures, we call a 'system'. Thus there are inorganic, organic, sociological, and technical systems . . ." to which we would like to add, aesthetic systems. Wieser continued: "If we say that the concept of structure in the natural sciences is gaining in importance in our time, then this means that even such natural occurrences, which we previously tended to conceive of as linear processes, can only be explained as the result of the complex interdependence of numerous elements. Particles and linear processes are the result of dissection and abstraction and are never representative of the whole. The basis of all of this is the phennomenon of organization. Organization is a principle which cannot be traced back to the two categories of energy and matter; it is itself an independent magnitude, neither energy nor substance, but a third, which expresses itself through the degree and the kind of order (or negative entropy) of a system. Norbert Wiener, among others, formulated this about ten years ago, but it is undeniable that the basic features of these ideas lead back to the problem of form as Plato and Aristotle conceived of it."[11]

These thoughts have a direct bearing on modern aesthetics which makes the complexity of organization in an aesthetic system one of its main arguments, and understands the qualities of the aesthetic as against the physical world process to be the degree of order, the improbability and the irregular distribution in the arrangement of the pictorial form (Bense, among others). These qualities

Fig. 11. Otto Piene (born 1928). *Calm*, 1960. Oil on canvas, 80 x 100 cm. Private Collection.

evidently can only be grasped structurally, and are particularly prominent in concrete art. That an organizational system causes an improbable distribution of the elements which are to be ordered only seems to be a paradox, but it points conclusively to the procedure of the creative artist. Besides, this idea has something in common with the classical approach to the interpretation of art, which has as its criterion the originality of a composition, the newness of its form and its motif.

To return to the definition of structure: Kant, whose philosophy ended the predominance of ontology over epistemology, and Wieser, a biologist concerned with cybernetics, both agree that structure is the unalterable configuration onto which the natural as well as artificial world, in its real as well as intellectual dimensions, has been attached. Both definitions point to the fact that structure is not some rigid condition, but that it creates itself, that it develops out of different kinds and differently interpretable forces. Similar explanations can be found in other fields, especially in physics, chemistry, logic, sociology and psychology.

The Concept of Structure in Psychology and Sociology

The manner in which psychology and sociology employ structural methods is very revealing in this context. They not only practice dissections, but with the knowledge of the structure evaluate the entirety of the appearance, which in this case is man (Adolf Portmann does the same thing in his morphological studies of animals).

In psychology, structure is considered to be one of the attributes of the form; according to Wolfgang Metzger, one of the most important investigators in this field in Germany, it is the first of three: "The structure (the 'tectonic'): to this belong the qualities of arrangement or of construction; the form of the space or the figural structure, the profile of the lightness and color including the arrangement and balancing of weight; rhythm, melody, sequence where there is movement and change. Examples: straight, round, jagged; legato, staccato, glissando, crescendo; constant, inconstant; the growing, shrinking, rising, falling, flowing, leaping; in short, any kind of 'transition'. . . ." One notices that these attributes are also used in the description of works of art and that they become increasingly more important with the disappearance of the "realistic" frame of reference. Among his examples Metzger also cites certain musical terms, and music, of course, is the purest, the classical example of the structural ordering of an aesthetic system. Metzger goes on to say: "A particularly important sub-class is that of the dynamic structures: the direction, the distribution, the 'structure' of the tension, attraction, repulsion, pressure, stress, impulse, including their changes with time; of their birth, their alterations, their disappearance. Such a state of tension can suggest itself even in a simple geometric figure, as has been shown in numerous investigations."[12]

Kandinsky has examined these in his theory of art, that is, the laws which determine the combination of geometric figures in painting and what intellectual impulses these laws radiate to the observer. Talking about the square in *Punkt und Linie zur Flaeche*,[13] he contends that it is a static element, influenced by different forces. As the primordial element of painting Kandinsky designates the point which had been defined through concentric tension. This point combines with similarly complicated structures; these in turn are related to the plane on which they are situated, as energies which mutually oppose and attract each other, and which enter into the harmony of the painting, the order given it by the artist.

Metzger mentions as further classes of formal attributes the "quality of wholeness" or "kind", and finally the "essence . . . in the extended sense in which it is used in the new theory of expression (*Klages,* 1942), where it is not only employed for living things but for every phenomenon. To the essential qualities here belong the physiognomical or expressive qualities: character, ethos, habitus, mood, and more of the same." "Essence" in other words is the interpretable "physiognomy" of the work of art, a value which can not be determined with exactness. For the psychological investigations, however, Metzger puts the emphasis on the "primacy of the structural qualities. . . . What is decisive for the scientific treatment of these facts is that only structural qualities can be registered and communicated, while the qualities of wholeness, of kind, and especially of essence can only be pointed out and no one who is not receptive to them can be forced to see them." With regard to the view one takes of works of art, he adds that ". . . the real advance of aesthetics, also with regard to the comprehension of essential qualities, is indebted to an investigation of structure. This retrogression to the structure, of course, is not the only task of aesthetic research, but in any case, after a purely phenomenological pointing out of an essential quality it is the indispensable next step."[12] Nothing else need be added to this.

Real and Possible Structures

The methodological combination of structural arrangements from the different fields of research would be given by the theory of structures as part of morphology. In morphology, i.e., in the doctrine of forms, structure is treated generally as the basis for the wholeness of the appearance, of their formations and transformations; one can also say, as their prerequisite. The structural investigation into the natural sciences is directed toward the explanation of the purpose behind the construction of the form, toward the factual functioning. It is the same in sociological and psychological investigation whose subject is mankind.

In connection with technology, the structural, i.e. the morphological method of investigation has undergone an enlargement and hypothetically includes not only the extant figures and forms but also the possible and probable phenomena. Max Bill has transferred this hypothetical morphology to the field of aesthetics, and into the shaping of the environment in general, where the problem also is to "invent" the form; in technology for practical purposes, in art for the intellectual use, in the shaping of the general environment as a connection between both the components. Again we are reminded of the conception of mastering the world by means of inventing the world, which realizes itself so clearly in an art which constantly is creating new means for itself.

The structural view of art, especially of painting, runs parallel, as we have seen, with the development of modern non-figurative art since the turn of the century. Wilhelm Worringer already emphasized in 1907 in his treatise *Abstraktion und Einfuehlung* the decisive position of the formal structure in the visual arts, contending that one could only speak of aesthetics in connection with formal laws. "The aesthetic effect can only issue forth from that higher condition which we call form, and whose essence is to conform to certain rules, no matter whether this conformity is simple and easily discernible, or whether it is differentiated in such a way that it can only be sensed as the conformity of the organic."[14)

Structural painting, whose objectives we attempted to delineate here, strives for that higher condition, which we call form, within the framework of a rational and critical understanding of the world, and with this confirms its actuality.

1. Georg Wilhelm Hegel, *Aesthetik*. Aufbau Verlag Berlin (1955).
2. Hans Arp, *Unsern taeglichen Traum*. Verlag der Arche Zurich (1955).
3. Piet Mondrian, *Plastic art and pure plastic art and other essays 1941-43. The Documents of Modern Art*. Wittenborn & Co. New York (1945).
4. Kasimir Malevitsch, *Die gegendstandslose Welt*. Bauhausbuecher No. 11. Verlag Albert Langen Munich (1927).
5. Paul Klee, *Das bildnerische Denken. Schriften zur Form—und Gestaltungslehre*. Benno Schwabe und Co. Basel/Stuttgart (1956). Published and edited by Juerg Spiller.
6. Guillaume Apollinaire, *Die Maler des Kubismus*. Verlag der Arche Zurich (1956).
7. Theo van Doesburg, *AC, Numéro d'Introduction du Groupe et de la Revue Art Concret*. Paris (1930).
8. Max Bill, *Worte rund um Malerei und Plastik*. Allianz-Katalog Kunsthaus Zurich (1947); revised 1958.
9. Max Bill, Introductory text in the catalogue of the exhibition *Enzo Mari*. Milan (1959). In German in *Augenblick*, IV, No. 2 (1960).
10. Max Bense, *Aesthetik und Zivilisation. Theorie der aesthetischen Kommunikation. Aesthetica III*. Agis Verlag Krefeld und Baden-Baden (1958).
11. Wolfgang Wieser, *Organismen, Strukturen, Maschinen*. Fischer-Buecherei, No. 230 (1959).
12. Wolfgang Metzger, *Psychologie. Entwicklung iher Grundannahmen seit der Einfuehrung des Experiments*. Dietrich Steinhoff-Verlag Darmstadt (1954).
13. Wassily Kandinsky, *Punkt und Linie zur Flaeche—Beitraege zur Analyse der modernen Malerei*. Third edition. Benteli-Verlag Bern-Buemplitz (1955), with an introduction by Max Bill.
14. Wilhelm Worringer, *Abstraktion und Einfuehlung*. R. Piper & Co. Munich. New edition 1959.

BIOGRAPHICAL NOTES ON THE AUTHORS

Max Bill

Architect, painter, sculptor and teacher. Born Winterthur, Switzerland, 1908. 1927–29: studied at Bauhaus, Dessau. 1936 and 1951 designer of Swiss Pavilion, Triannale, Milan. 1951: First International Grand Prix for sculpture, Biennale, Sao Paulo. 1950–56: co-founder Hochschule fuer Gestaltung, Ulm, Germany, for which he planned teaching program and designed buildings; director of school and head of departments of architecture and design. 1963–64: Director of cultural activities Swiss National Exhibition, Lausanne, 1964. Major publications: *Quinze Variations sur un même thème* (1936); *Le Corbusier et Pierre Jeanneret, 1934–38* (1938); *Robert Maillart* (1949); *Form—A balance sheet of mid-twentieth-century trends in design* (1952); edition of Kandinsky's writings.

Jacob Bronowski

Mathematician. Born 1908. Studied Jesus College, Cambridge; 1934–42 Senior Lecturer, University College, Hull. 1946–50: statistical research into economics of building and other industries, Ministry of Works. 1948: Head of Projects, UNESCO. 1950–59: Director of Coal Research Est., National Coal Board. 1953: Carnegie Visiting Professor, M.I.T. 1963: Visiting Fellow, Salk Institute. In addition to numerous mathematical papers, author of: *William Blake, a Man Without a Mask* (1944); *The Common Sense of Science* (1951); *The Face of Violence* (1954); *Science and Human Values* (1958); *The Western Intellectual Tradition* (1960).

R. Buckminster Fuller

Engineer and inventor. Born Milton, Mass., 1895. Studied Harvard and U. S. Naval Acad. 1932: Founder, director and chief engineer Dymaxion Corp., Bridgeport, Conn. 1954–: President, Geodesics, Inc. 1957–: Polydomes, Inc., Des Moines, Iowa. 1955–59: President, Synergetics, Inc., Raleigh, N. C. Inventor and developer of large clear span structural enclosures. Initiated research, development, and university lectures in Dymaxion Technology. Visiting professor and lecturer in energetic geometry at major universities, 1955–59. Introduced Geodesic Structures at many universities and colleges. Builder of Geodesic structures, designer and producer of radomes and air deliverable pavilions for international world fairs.

Richard Held

Psychologist. Born New York, 1922. Studied Columbia Univ., Swarthmore College, and Harvard. 1950–51: Teaching Fellow, Harvard. 1955–59: Institute for Advanced Studies, Princeton. 1958–62: Professor of Psychology, Brandeis Univ. 1962–63: Senior Research Fellow, National Science Foundation. Since 1963 Professor of Experimental and Developmental Psychology, M.I.T. Particularly interested in the history of, and assumptions behind, formulations of problems of perception. Large number of papers in major journals of psychology.

H. L. C. Jaffé

Art Historian. Born Frankfurt, 1915. Studied Univ. of Amsterdam. Formerly assistant director Amsterdam Municipal Museum. Since 1961 Director Jewish Historical Museum, Amsterdam, and also, since 1963 Extraordinarius Professor Modern and Contemporary History of Art, Univ. of Amsterdam. Major publications: *de Stijl, 1917–1931, the Dutch contribution to modern art* (1956); *Het probleem der werkelijkheid in de kunst der XXe eeuw* (1958); *Inleiding tot de Kunst van Mondrian* (1959); *Kunst van heden in het stedelijk* (introd. by W. J. H. B. Sandberg) (1961); *De schilderkunst van de XXe eeuw* (1963).

Gyorgy Kepes	Painter and designer. Born Selyp, Hungary, 1906. 1930–36 worked in Berlin and London on film, stage, and exhibition design. In 1937 came to the United States to head the Light and Color Department, Institute of Design, Chicago. Since 1946 Professor of Visual Design, M. I. T. Author: *Language of Vision* and *The New Landscape in Art and Science*. Editor: *The Visual Arts Today*.
Richard Lippold	Sculptor and teacher. Studied at Art Institute of Chicago and Univ. of Chicago. Worked as designer. Began in 1942 to devote himself to sculpture. Taught at Univ. of Michigan, Goddard College, Trenton Jr. College and from 1952 Assoc. Professor Hunter College. One-man shows, Willard Gallery, N. Y. 1947, '48, '50, '52. Works represented: Addison Gallery, Andover, Mass.; Munson-Williams-Proctor Institute, Utica, N. Y.; Wadsworth Atheneum, Hartford, Conn.; Metropolitan Museum of Art, N. Y. C.; Detroit Institute of Arts. Important recent works for Philharmonic Hall, Lincoln Center and Pan-Am Building, N. Y.
Fumihiko Maki Masato Ohtaka	Both architects of Japan and members of the "Metabolism" group, whose main activity is to promote and develop a new urban planning in Japan. Maki was born in 1928. Studied at the Univ. of Tokyo and Harvard. From 1956–61 taught at Washington Univ., St. Louis, and then at Harvard, where he has been Professor of City Planning since 1963. Ohtaka was born in 1923. Studied at the Univ. of Tokyo. Currently lecturer at Waseda Univ. and practicing architect in Tokyo. Both are co-authors of *Metabolism 1960*.
Pier Luigi Nervi	Engineer, architect and Professor of Technology and Construction Techniques, Univ. of Rome. Pioneer in use of reinforced concrete in architecture. 1920: formed partnership, Nervi and Nebbiosi. Important works executed at this time: Municipal Stadium, Florence, finished 1932. 1932: formed partnership, Nervi and Bartoli, design and construction firm which he still heads. Airplane hangars, built 1938–43, won the firm international recognition. Mid-40's developed "Ferro-cemento", system of layers of fine steel mesh sprayed with cement mortar. The great practical importance and aesthetic possibilities of this material fully realized in Grand Salone, Exhibition Hall, Turin (1948–49). Among important recent works: buildings for 1960 Olympics, Rome. Author: *Arte o scienza del Costruire* (1945); *Costruire correttamente* (1954), English translation entitled *Structures* (1956).
I. A. Richards	Writer, educator and poet. Born, Cheshire, England, 1893. Studied at Cambridge Univ., where he collaborated with C. K. Ogden on *The Meaning of Meaning*, published 1923. Since 1944 University Professor, Harvard Univ. Major publications: *The Principles of Literary Criticism* (1924); *Coleridge on Imagination* (1934); *The Philosophy of Rhetoric* (1936); *Interpretation in Teaching* (1938); *How to Read a Page* (1942); *Nations and Peace* (1947); *Speculative Instruments* (1955); *Goodbye Earth, and Other Poems* (1958); *The Screens and Other Poems* (1958).
Eduard F. Sekler	Architect and architectural historian. Born Vienna, 1920. Studied Vienna and Warburg Institute, London. Since 1956 Professor of History and Theory of Architecture and Urban Design, Harvard. Since 1962 Coordinator of Studies, Carpenter Center of the Visual Arts, Harvard. Architectural work: Vienna and New York (Austrian Institute). Restoration of historical monuments. Major publications: *Point Houses in European Architecture* (1952); *Wren and His Place in European Architecture* (1956).

Cyril Stanley Smith	Metallurgist. Born, Birmingham, England, 1903. Studied at Birmingham and M.I.T. 1943–46: associate division leader in charge of metallurgy, Manhattan Project, Los Alamos Scientific Lab. 1946–56: Director, Institute to Study Metals, Univ. of Chicago. 1946–61: Professor of Metallurgy, Univ. of Chicago. Since 1961, Institute Professor of Metallurgy and History of Technology and Science, M.I.T. Major interests and research: role of interface energy and topology in structure of polycrystalline materials; historical interaction between science and technology; oriental metal working techniques. Author of *A History of Metallography* (1960).
Alison and Peter Smithson	Architects. Born 1928 and 1923. Studied at School of Architecture (Univ. of Durham), Newcastle-upon-Tyne. Built works: Hunstanton Secondary Modern School, 1950–54; private houses, 1954–63; Iraqi Airways Building, 1961; Economist, 1960–64. Major projects: Golden Lane, City of London "Deck" Housing, 1952; Cluster projects at Isolate; hamlet, village, town and city scale for CIAM team X meetings, 1956; University, college and school projects, 1954, '58, '59; Hauptstadt, Berlin, 1957–58; London Road Study, 1959; Wettbewerb Steilshoop, Hamburg, 1961; Cambridge Citizens Plan, 1962. Publications include theoretical studies of "Town Building" in *Architectural Design, Architectural Review* and *Architect's Year Book*.
Margit Staber	Art critic. Born, Neu-Ulm, Germany. Studied Hochschule fuer Gestaltung, Ulm. Lives in Zurich. Collaborator in studio of Max Bill. Regular contributor: *Art International; Zodiac; Pagina; New Graphic Design; Form; Neue Zuercher Zeitung*. Guest Editor Walker Art Center, Minneapolis. Monographic essays: on Max Bill, Hans Scharoun, Walter Schwagenscheidt (*Zodiac,* 9, 10, 12), Josef Albers (*New Graphic Design* 17/18), and Marcel Duchamp (*Kunstwerk,* 7/XIV/61). Monograph: *Max Bill* (1964). Preparation of Catalogues: *Concrete Art,* Zuercher Kunstgesellschaft, Zurich (1960), *Georges Vantongerloo,* Marlborough Gallery, London (1962).
Lancelot Law Whyte	Physicist. Born Edinburgh, 1896. Senior Scholar Trinity College, Cambridge. Late '20's in Berlin as a Rockefeller Fellow in Physics. 1930's associated with investment bank as scientific consultant on financing new inventions. Later managing director, Power Jets, Ltd., which developed the Whittle jet engine. 1941–1945, Director of Statistical Enquiries, Ministry of Supplies. Has since devoted his time to writing and lecturing. Major publications: *Archimedes, or the Future of Physics* (1927); *Critique of Physics* (1931); *The Next Development in Man* (1944); *Everyman looks forward* (1946); *The Unitary Principle in Physics and Biology* (1949); *Aspects of Form* (edited) (1951); *Accent on Form* (1955); *The Atomic Problem* (1961); *R. J. Boscovich,* 1711–1787 (edited) (1961); *Essays on Atomism, Democritus to 1960* (1961); *The Unconscious before Freud* (1962).

Designed by the arts staff, George Braziller, Inc.
Printed in offset by Connecticut Printers, Inc., Hartford, Conn.

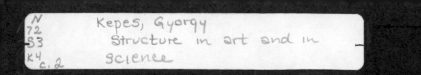